EVOLUTION OR CREATION

PROF. H. ENOCH, M.A., F.Z.S.

EVOLUTION

OR

CREATION

With a foreword by
SIR CECIL WAKELEY,
K.B.E., C.B., LL.D., M.Ch., D.Sc., F.R.C.S.

 EVANGELICAL PRESS

P.O. Box 5, Welwyn, Herts., England AL6 9NU
P.O. Box 2453, Grand Rapids, Mich. 49501, U.S.A.

© Union of Evangelical Students of India

First Indian Edition 1966

First British Edition 1967

Reprinted 1968

Revised and enlarged edition 1976

ISBN 0 85234 073 7

Cover design by PETER WAGSTAFF

Printed in Great Britain by Stanley L. Hunt (Printers) Ltd.,
Rushden, Northamptonshire

CONTENTS

FOREWORD

I am very pleased to comply with the wish of Professor H. Enoch and write a foreword to his excellent book.

The time has come for all thoughtful people to make up their minds about the creation of the world.

Scripture is quite definite that God created the world and I for one believe that to be a fact, not fiction. There is no evidence, scientific or otherwise, to support the theory of evolution. Yet, the scientific world and our Universities and Schools still teach evolution. I sincerely trust that this book will play its part, all over the world, in exposing the unproved theory of evolution and establishing the proved Biblical fact of the Creation of mankind. Evolution is a man-made theory. Creation came by the hand of Almighty God.

Cecil Wakeley

K.B.E., C.B., LL.D., M.CH., D.SC., F.R.C.S.

Fellow of King's College, London.
Past President, Royal College of Surgeons of England.
Consulting Surgeon: King's College Hospital, Belgrave Hospital for Children, Royal Masonic Hospital and the Royal Navy.
President of the Bible League.

FOREWORD

ABOUT THE AUTHOR

Professor H. Enoch, born in Trivandrum (Kerala State) India is a graduate of the University of Madras. He later became professor and head of the Zoology Department in this same university and on his retirement he had over 30 years' experience teaching university students.

He has travelled extensively, both in the East and in the West, acquainting himself with some of the original materials on which the theory of organic evolution is founded.

For many years he was president of the Union of Evangelical Students of India and Vice-Chairman of the International Fellowship of Evangelical Students.

THE TESTIMONY OF THE AUTHOR

The main reason for writing this book is to help the readers, particularly University students and teachers, to see that the Bible is the Word of God, and that the Genesis record of creation can be relied upon even in this modern age of science. Having been in touch with University students, particularly students of biology, for more than three decades, the author is aware of the spiritual dangers that surround them in the Universities. This volume is written mainly to enable them to give a reason for their faith in the Bible.

The question of Evolution *versus* Creation has been a great problem in the writer's life, and his only incentive to write this book is a desire to give the benefit of his own personal experience to others. When studying natural science and zoology his Christian faith was challenged by the theory of Organic Evolution which was believed and taught by the leading biologists of the day. His first reaction was to accept the theory of evolution as a fact, and to reconcile it with the Biblical teaching by treating the account of creation recorded in the first chapter of Genesis as a story mainly intended to teach a spiritual lesson, rather than as a scientific treatise. As he was convinced of the truth of a spiritual world and the veracity of the words of the Lord Jesus Christ in the New Testament regarding creation, his only way of escape was to effect a compromise by believing in a Theistic Evolution. According to this view, God created all the animals and plants in this world through a process of evolution, man alone being His special creation.

In this belief the writer rested for a time. But a deeper spiritual experience, after his college course, shook his faith in the Theory of Evolution altogether. His spiritual "eyes" were opened to see that he had a fallen nature and consequently needed redemption. All his doubt regarding the existence of a personal God and the veracity of His book, the Bible, vanished, and he saw that he must "let God be *true* and every man a liar". This made him study the Theory of Evolution afresh, this time with a critical mind, weighing every argument for and against the theory. He also had the privilege of visiting various countries, both in the East and in the West, and seeing and examining for himself some of the original materials and exhibits meant to support the theory of evolution. This critical study of the subject has driven him to the conclusion that the theory of evolution is not an established fact, and there is no definite proof that animals and plants have come to their present stage through such a process rather than by creation as stated in the Bible. This conviction has been further established by the accumulation of scientific facts that have come to light since then. Now it is his considered opinion that all known scientific facts can be fittingly accommodated only in terms of creation. What is written in Exodus 20: 11 – "For in six days the Lord made heaven and earth, the sea, and all that in them is, and rested on the seventh day" cannot be contradicted by any established scientific fact.

The writer is also convinced of the truth of John 3: 16 – "God so loved the world, that He gave His only begotten Son, that whosoever believeth in Him should not perish, but have everlasting life". He has experienced the power of this God in his own life. Therefore he is "not ashamed of the gospel of Christ, for it is the power of God unto salvation to everyone that believeth" (Romans 1: 16).

This book is published with the hope that many will find the peace and rest which their Creator, the Lord Jesus Christ, came to give, and that when they find this they will no longer be ashamed of the written Word of God, even in this modern age of science.

H. Enoch
Madras
20th December, 1965.

PREFACE TO FIRST EDITION

One reason for the publication of this volume is the desire of the author to set before the public the truth of the Word of God as against the erroneous philosophy of evolution. Having been a Professor of Zoology for more than thirty years, and having taught the subject in more than one University in India, the writer, as a committed Christian, feels a great responsibility to place before the public the benefits of his own study and experience.

It is the writer's hope that as students read this book, which presents facts against the theory of evolution, they will keep an open mind and seek for truth. By weighing the evidence for and against the theory, they can arrive at their own conclusions, rather than be carried away by the sheer weight of so-called "scientific" statements. The writer also hopes that many Christians will be strengthened in their faith in the Bible, knowing that there is factual evidence for "the faith once delivered unto the saints".

The author claims no originality in this work and wishes to acknowledge his great indebtedness to the many soldiers of Christ who not only fought a good fight to maintain the faith, but also carried the battle into the enemy's camp. He wishes to express his indebtedness to the publications of the Evolution Protest Movement of England, to the writings of the late Professor McReady Price, to Byron Nelson, Frank Marsh, and H. B. Morris, and to the literature of the

"Creation Research Society". He also wishes to thank Mr. D. C. C. Watson, who went through the articles when they were first published, for his very valuable suggestions.

His thanks are due to the Union of Evangelical Students of India for the encouragement given him to write such a volume, and to the publishers for seeing it through the press.

This book goes out with the prayers of many that it may point every reader to the Creator, Who came in flesh into this world to give peace and salvation to all who put their trust in Him.

H. Enoch
Madras, 1965.

PREFACE TO SECOND EDITION

Judging from the innumerable letters of appreciation received from many parts of the world, some even from communists, the author has some satisfaction in believing that this book, though so small and insignificant, has met a long felt need. There is a growing demand for it both in India and in England and inspite of the reprints we have not been able to meet the demand. In fact, according to the publishers the stock is now completely exhausted. Before reprinting the same book, there was a suggestion that a new revised edition be published, incorporating some of the additional facts of science which have come to light since first publishing this book in 1966. It is with this object in view that this new revised edition is published.

New facts of science which do not find a place in the older reprints are now included in the body of the text. In addition a new chapter (chapter 17) is added, dealing with the modern scientific methods of dating the fossils etc., in relation to Biblical records. The author is not a competent authority in determining the age of the earth or this universe, but he feels the responsibility to enlighten the public with the conclusions arrived at by competent men of authority; the results of their latest scientific investigations. These tend to indicate the young age of the earth, which fact obviously goes counter to the theory of Evolution. On the other hand it supports the Biblical record of creation and its subsequent history. It is for this reason that a new chapter is added to this edition. The writer wishes to acknowledge his great debt of gratitude to the Creation Research Society and its contributors. But for their help the addenda could not have been prepared. His prayer is that truth which is eternal may be established.

"Thy word is true from the beginning" – Psalm 119: 160.

H. Enoch
19, Ritherdon Road,
Madras-7.
12th February, 1974.

Chapter i

MORPHOLOGY
AND COSMOGONY

It shall be the writer's endeavour to weigh the so-called "evidences" for the theory of evolution in the balance of truth, allowing the reader to draw his own conclusions. "Evolution in very simple terms," according to the *Houston Post*, "means that life progressed from one celled organisms to its highest state, the human being, by means of a series of biological changes taking place over millions of years."[1] But according to Haldane and Huxley, Evolution is a "self-starting and self-improving process" without any supernatural intervention. Special pains have been taken to give quotations, mainly from supporters of the theory so that it may be condemned from the mouth of its friends. One by one the various so-called "evidences" will be stated in all fairness to the evolutionist, giving the scientific facts on which they are based and their probable interpretation from a Biblical point of view. The reader is requested to do his own thinking and judge for himself whether the "evidences" are convincing.

MORPHOLOGICAL EVIDENCE

(a) *Evidence from Classification*—In his study of the various organisms in nature, the evolutionist finds some organisms to be very simple in structure and others more complicated. He finds it possible to arrange or classify these organisms in a fairly graded system from the most simple to the most complex, or, as he would put it, from the "lowest" to the

I

"highest". Thus he places a single-celled animal like *amoeba* first, and next to it or "above" it the multicellular *hydra*, and next to it a three-layered worm, and next to it *amphioxus*, and then a fish, an amphibian, a reptile and a lower ape. Next to that a higher ape, and lastly the most complex of all—Man. When he has finished arranging these creatures in that order, from the simpler to the more complicated, he turns to the creationist and says: "See, here is a proof for the theory of evolution, showing how the complicated evolved out of the simpler ones!"

This is a strange proof indeed? Such proofs are not wanting in any sphere of life, for simple and complicated things which lend themselves to such arrangements exist everywhere. By arranging his books on a shelf in a graded system, depending on the size or complexity of its contents, a student can also prove the "evolution" of his books. The reader may well see the absurdity of such an argument, for it assumes the very thing to be proved. Nevertheless it has deceived thousands of students in the past and is still deceiving thousands more who allow themselves to be carried away by sheer weight of "scientific authority", instead of thinking for themselves clearly and logically.

In his book *A Critique of Evolution Theory* the late well-known evolutionist T. H. Morgan of Columbia University admits that the proof from classification is in fact no real proof at all. On page nine of the same book he says that when the fallacy of the argument is pointed out to pupils of his who believe in evolution, they are resentful. We may boldly affirm that this proof is absurd; and the fact that organisms can be arranged in a certain order does not preclude the possibility of both the simple and the complex coming into existence simultaneously. The Bible says that all animal life was created in two days (Genesis 1: 20-27). Also, *"For in six days the Lord made the heaven and the earth, the sea and all that in them is, and rested the seventh day: wherefore the Lord blessed the sabbath day, and hallowed it"*.[2] With God such things are possible.

(b) *Proof from Comparative Anatomy* – When a student of anatomy studies the structure of various animals in detail such as the bones, the muscles, the arteries, the veins, etc., it becomes apparent to him that there is a certain similarity of structure underlying them all. For example the anatomy of cat, dog, monkey and man resemble each other a great deal, taking bone for bone, muscle for muscle, and nerve for nerve, even to the smallest detail. It may also be stated that the resemblance between the animals themselves varies. Thus a cat resembles a dog more than a monkey, and a monkey resembles a man more than it resembles a dog. Based on this similarity of structure, animals can be arranged in a fairly graded system. Again, comparing the anatomy of the wing of a bird, the paddle of a whale and the arm of a man it is observed that they are all constructed on the same general plan taking bone for bone, muscle for muscle and nerve for nerve. The evolutionist contends that such similarity of structure can be explained only on the basis of evolution, namely, that they all had a common ancestor.

Similarity of structure is a scientific fact, for one can observe it in studying the anatomy of these animals. But the interpretation put on this similarity can reasonably be denied. For this similarity of structure can with equal reasonableness be used as an argument in favour of the doctrine of special creation. For instance, if the various colleges of the city were compared, one would be sure to find many points of similarity. Each may have an entrance, an office room, a Principal's room, a library with books, class rooms with blackboards and seating arrangements, etc. This comparison may be extended even to minor details, to show that the resemblance between two Science Colleges is greater than the resemblance between an Arts College and a Science College. But from this similarity of structure it cannot be argued that the biggest (first grade) Science College building came out of a smaller (second grade) Science College building or that both Science and Arts College buildings evolved out of a common ancestor! For we know that they

were all constructed separately. Yet they may well have
been planned and constructed by one architect at one and
the same time. Similarity in design in the case of colleges
does not prove their evolution; neither does similarity of
design prove evolution in the case of living organisms. To
the believer in the Bible, similarity in plan of structure
among living organisms merely establishes the fact of one
great Architect, the Creator, who had in mind one great
pattern which He used while making His natural species
with such modifications as were necessary for their different
conditions of life. He could as well have created them all on
different patterns, the dog with four legs, the cat with five,
the cow with six and the elephant with nineteen! He could
have put the nostrils of the monkey behind its ears and given
man two heads! But as they all have to live upon the same
earth, breathing the same air and drinking the same kind of
water, it was but reasonable that a wise Creator should
construct them all on a similar pattern, allowing modifications wherever necessary. Thus similarity of structure, as
revealed in comparative anatomy, may as well point to a
common Creator as to any evolutionary process.

However, this similarity of structure seen in the anatomy
of the arm of man, the paddle of a whale and the wing of
a bird is only superficial. A deeper study, such as by chemical
analysis of the very substance with which these limbs are
made, reveals marked divergencies. When the cytoplasm of
the cells of the different animals is centrifuged, it breaks up
into particles known as "centrifugates". Some of this dis-
sociated matter of cytoplasm forms jelly-like pellets known
as "particulates". These particulates on analysis show that
their chemical make-up differs according to the species
under investigation. The formula of the particulates of
each species differs from the formula of all other species.
There is one formula for the bird, another for the whale,
another for the ape and another for man. All mankind
belongs to one species and has one formula, for *"God hath
made of one blood all nations of men that dwell upon the face*

of the earth", as the Bible says. He never used the same formula for any two different species on earth.

This is a very significant revelation brought to light through one of the youngest of sciences, known as cyto-chemistry. This revelation is not only unfavourable to the theory of evolution but it positively confirms the idea of creation of each kind or natural species. *"Kind"* or *"Baramin"* (created kind) so named by Dr. Frank L. Marsh is a definite classificatory term – a unit of creation according to the Bible. Cross breeding between two individuals of the same "kind" would be possible but not between two of different "kinds". The term *"species"* is not the "kind" referred to in Genesis. "Species" according to Seigler's opinion must be regarded as *artificial units* derived from the created kind due to *degeneration* of the original genetic pool and not due to progressive evolution.[3] If animals transgress beyond this they become sterile or degenerate into extinction. The Bible says, *"And God said, Let the waters bring forth abundantly the moving creature that hath life, and fowl that may fly above the earth in the open firmament of heaven. And God created great whales and every living creature that moveth, which the waters brought forth abundantly after their kind, and every winged fowl after his kind: and God saw that it was good. And God blessed them saying, Be fruitful and multiply and fill the waters in the seas, and let fowl multiply in the earth"* (Genesis 1: 20-22).

COSMOGONY

The late Professor Bateson of Cambridge University in his article in *Nature*, dated 20th August, 1914, page 638, declared that every theory of evolution must be such as to accord with the facts of Physics and Chemistry – a prime necessity to which our predecessors paid small heed. Studying the facts of Physics and Astronomy one comes to the conclusion arrived at by the late Professor James Jeans that *"the universe is like a clock running down"*. Thus the sun burns out two hundred and fifty million tons of matter per minute, and we do not know how long the process will continue. Again, thorium disintegrates into radium, and finally becomes lead. The complex stars break down into nebulae in a few hours' time, as observed at present, and not in millions of years as was once believed.

J. W. N. Sullivan in his *Limitation of Science* says: "One of the least disputable laws of Physical Science states that the universe is steadily running down . . . we live in a wasting universe. . . . But the fact that the energy of the universe will be more disorganised tomorrow than it is today implies, of course, that the energy of the universe was more highly organised yesterday than it is today. Following the process backward, we find a more and more highly organised universe. This backward tracing of time cannot be continued indefinitely. Organisation cannot, as it were, mount up and up without limit. There is a definite maximum, and this definite maximum must have been in existence a finite time ago. And it is impossible that this state of perfect organisation could have been evolved from some less perfect state. Nor is it possible that the universe could have persisted from eternity in that state of perfect organisation and suddenly, a finite time ago, have begun to pursue its present path. Thus the accepted laws of nature lead us to a definite beginning of the universe in time. We are to suppose, on this reasoning, that at some particular moment in the past a perfectly organised universe sprang suddenly into being, and has steadily become more and more degraded ever since." Sullivan further states that "it is still more startling, almost incredible, when we reflect that this panorama sprang suddenly into existence a finite time ago. It emerged fully armed, as it were, out of nothing, apparently for the purpose of blazing its way to an eternal death. This is the scientific account."

This statement is in full agreement with the recent (1965) discovery of new facts by the American Astronomer Dr. Allan Sandage, of Mount Palomar, California. According to him the universe had a definite beginning and it will not last forever. He is of the opinion that the "steady state" theory of Professor Fred. Hoyle, who believes that there is a constant creation of new stars in space from hydrogen atoms, is all wrong. Thus recent scientific opinion seems to support the idea of a definite creation of the Universe in time and its gradual disintegration, rather than the evolution of a Universe out of nothing. God's word in Genesis 1: 1 seems to be more scientific! Thus in physics and astronomy we see *the complicated becoming simpler*, not the simpler evolving into the more complicated.

Turning now to Zoology, we have already shown that the fact that animals admit of arrangement in a graded system according to their complexity does not establish the theory that the complicated came out of the simpler ones. And judging from the phenomena observable elsewhere in Nature, it might well be argued with equal reasonableness that the complicated degenerated into the simpler forms; and the graded system seen among animals is due to de-volution rather than to evolution. The reader may decide for himself whether either of these theories are as probable as the Bible doctrine, God's creation of each "natural" species.

VESTIGIAL ORGANS

Another proof from Morphology offered by the evolutionist is the presence of so-called "vestigial organs" in certain animals. Vestigial organs, according to Professor H. H. Newman, are "useless representatives of organs which, in other allied kinds of animals, are functional". In the bodies of animals it is said that there are parts which have no function at all, but which functioned in their ancestors and became vestigial in their descendants, according to the theory of evolution. The higher the animal the greater the number of such vestigial organs found; and man being the highest is supposed to carry a lot of "useless" luggage about him (nearly 180 organs, according to Weidersham). Of these we may consider a few outstanding examples which are often cited as "proofs" by the evolutionist.

Before proceeding further it is well for us to remember that in view of the fact that all creatures on this earth have to breathe the same air, drink the same water, and live by "internal combustion" of food, we should expect in the body of man the same muscles and organs which are found in the lower animals, only modified for human needs. This is exactly what is observed. For example, the muscles in the head of a horse are the same as those in a human head. But the function of these muscles is not exactly the same in each. The muscles by which the horse can move its ears, and vigorously twitch the skin of its forehead to drive away flies, are not so well developed in man; for the obvious reason that he has other means of driving them away. Nevertheless these muscles do move, and are responsible for most of his facial expressions. If these so-called "vestigial" muscles were removed from his head he would be able neither to laugh nor smile, nor visibly express other emotions. Likewise to call the ear muscles of man "vestigial" is to misrepresent the facts. Man does not move his ears as animals do (though some are capable of moving them!), but that does not prove that his ear muscles are useless. For if the ear muscles are removed there can be no proper circulation of the blood, and freezing of the ears may result in cold climates. Similarly there are many other organs in the human body, and some in lower animals, which the evolutionists consider to be useless. Let us examine a few of them.

(1) *The Coccyx*. This is the technical name for the last part of the vertebral column of man. According to the evolutionist it is the vestigial tail, turned inwards, which was functional at one stage of man's ascent up the zoological ladder. But in reality the coccyx is the fusion of the last four vertebrae, to which the important muscles of elimination are attached; and its removal would interfere directly or indirectly with defaecation. In all land vertebrates the primordia for the hind legs start at a point on the vertebral

column about eight or ten vertebrae from the end, and these posterior vertebrae are put to different uses in different animals – such as the tail in the monkey, or coccyx in man. The coccyx, therefore, has a definite function and can no longer be regarded as a vestigial organ.

(2) *The Endocrine Glands.* Such glands as the pituitary body, thyroid and thymus, and till very recently the pineal body also, were once considered to be vestigial or useless organs. But as Paley declared, "Our list of useless structures, decreases as our stock of knowledge increases" (as quoted by Sir Arthur Keith in *Concerning Man's Origin*, 1941, p. 147). Regarding the thymus and tonsils Sir Arthur, an evolutionist, declares that "no one would describe them as vestiges" in *Nature*, 12th December, 1925.

(3) *Vestigial Limbs.* Among the lower animals, the hind limbs and claws of the python are described as vestigial organs. But in fact these are real legs reduced by mutation. Other examples of the loss of limbs by mutation are well known. L. H. Snyden (1946) in *The Principles of Heredity*, third edition, p. 393, pictures a family in which the father and children have neither hands nor feet. Vestigial winged fruitflies are not the result of a series of gradual reductions but a transition by mutation in one generation. However, the claws of a python are used to propel its massive body along the ground, and also to inflict wounds on the victims, which the snake kills by winding itself around them. These claws are therefore useful to the python and cannot be considered vestigial.

Among the whales there are a few cartilaginous rods of about six to ten inches in length found embedded in the flesh without attachment to the spine. These structures occur between the anterior paddles and the tail flukes. These are pointed out as the whale's vestigial hind-limbs. They can also be bones of a reduced fin. But in fact these rods, which do not project outside the body, have a definite function: they support the genital and other organs of the monster, which is an aquatic mammal with tail flukes instead of hind-limbs. They cannot therefore be rightly called vestigial.

(4) *The Vermiform Appendix.* This is the narrow blind end of the "caecum" causing the disease known as appendicitis in man. In the lower animals, especially the herbivorous, it is of a large size; and evolutionists believe that it is one of the vestigial organs in man. Now regarding the exact function of the appendix, uncertainty still exists, but that it has a function is conceded by all thoughtful men. Sir Arthur Keith in *Nature* (loc. cit.) writes: "The appendix does not merit the name 'vestigial'. . . . It is never vestigial in a newly-born child, we have every reason to think that it is as well developed in a newly-born child of today as it was in children born 10,000 years ago, for it is scarcely larger in a newly-born anthropoid ape than in a newly-born child." Professor William Straus in *Quarterly Review of Biology*, 1947, p. 149, states that "there is no longer any justification for regarding the vermiform appendix as a vestigial structure". Yet Professor H. H. Newman in his text-book entitled *Evolution, Genetics and Eugenics* cites the appendix as an example of a vestigial organ. In this connection another interesting sidelight comes from the fact that the higher apes possess an appendix, whereas their less immediate relatives, the lower apes, do not; but it appears again among the still lower mammals such as the opossum. *How can the evolutionist account for this?*

However, the utter absurdity of calling the appendix "vestigial" in man is apparent above all from this fact: that its function is unknown not only in man but also in every other species of animal that possess it. It looks as though evolution has produced a totally useless organ all through the animal world; and evolutionists have now to explain how such a useless organ evolved through Natural Selection! The creationist on the other hand contends that the body of an animal is constructed to suit its environment and that it possesses no organ which is not useful at one time or another during its life-time. The evolutionist describes as vestigial any muscle or bone or tendon which is less developed in one species than another, or any organ whose function is unknown, or sometimes even the embryonic organs of Vialleton.

The Law of Vialleton (1924) or the *Law of Phyletic Isoschematism* states that the embryonic primordia have initially the same constitution and form in all animals of the same group. Thus every embryo has the rudiments of every organ of the group though some do not develop, e.g. the mammary glands in the male. The fact that the mammary glands are ill-developed in the male does not indicate that they are vestigial organs, which were once well developed and functional when the males suckled their young ones, but which became vestigial subsequently after relegating the function to the females! No. The existence of such undeveloped organs can well be explained by the law of *Phyletic Isoschematism* of Vialleton and the laws of mutation.

It is true that there are a few structures whose function is at present unknown; but to conclude rashly that such organs are useless, and to offer them as "proof" of evolution, is not at all scientific. Professor E. S. Goodrich in his *Evolution of Living Organisms* (1912), p. 68, declares: "He would be a rash man indeed who would now assert that any part of the human body is useless." Quite apart from this, the presence of vestigial organs, even if they should exist, would be more a proof of *devolution*, than of evolution.

In order to prove his theory the evolutionist ought to show the existence of *"nascent organs"*, i.e. organs newly acquired by an animal, and which did not exist in its ancestor. But not even a single nascent organ has been found in any living or fossil animal or plant. Everyone seems to have sprung into existence "fully armed" for the battle of life. If evolutionists had regard to the rules of giving evidence they would never cite vestigial organs as proofs of their theory, since nascent organs do not exist.

Hence we see that proof from the so-called "vestigial organs" is no proof at all, since no organ in any animal can with certainty be described as useless; and it is reasonable to expect that advancing research will in course of time discover to us the exact function of every single structure.

[1] *Houston Post*, 23rd August, 1964.
[2] Exodus 20: 11.
[3] See *Evolution or Degeneration* by Hilbert R. Steigler, 1972.

Chapter 2

PALAEONTOLOGY

In the present chapter we shall examine the evidence afforded by fossils, bearing in mind that it was mainly Darwin's confidence in Lyell's geology that led him to propound the theory of organic evolution.

According to evolutionists, palaeontology is the study of fossil remains of extinct animals and plants, including any traces of their existence such as foot-prints and impressions in slate, clay, or coal. T. H. Huxley wrote that "the primary and direct evidence in favour of evolution can be furnished *only by* palaeontology . . . if evolution has taken place, there will its mark be left: if it has not taken place, there will be its refutation". Again, T. H. Morgan in his *Critique of Evolution*, p. 24, declares that this evidence from the earth's strata is "by all odds the strongest evidence of the theory of evolution". Let us therefore examine this "strongest evidence!"

In many parts of the world along mountain sides, river banks, etc., earth layers or "strata" of various thicknesses can be observed lying horizontally one upon another. These layers were evidently made by the agency of water, the lowest being deposited first and the top layers last. Evolutionists tell us that the first deposit was laid about a billion years ago, and subsequent layers at intervals of hundreds of millions of years. At the same time a bit of protoplasm "somehow" came into existence and gradually evolved into the various groups of plants and animals

which have left their record in the rocks. Consequently in
the lower strata we find fossil remains of simple forms of
life, and in the topmost layers the more complex. This
constitutes the palaeontological argument in favour of
evolution. Let us therefore examine the nature of the strata
and the fossils they contain.

THE GEOLOGICAL COLUMN

Modern geologists divide the past into six eras; these are
sub-divided into about sixteen periods, each covering a span
of time which ranges from 25 to 90 million years. From the
Cambrian era to late Cenozoic this totals some 500 million
years. To this are added the Proterozoic and Archaeozoic
eras, which are not divided into periods, each covering
another 500 million years. These eras and periods are
arranged in a vertical sequence or "column" and published
in text-books. But it will be a shock to many students to
learn the fact that nowhere on the face of the earth does
such a column exist, that there is no spot where more than
two or three "systems" are found one above the other. As
Professor S. J. Bole, PH.D., Professor of Biology, has pointed
out: "Grabau states that it is of first importance that the
stratographer should find a continuous record, in order that
he may have a measure whereby to judge the partial
records. But there is no such continuous record. . . . The
type section of the time table is said to be 95 miles thick.
But the thickness of the stratified rocks in any place varies
from less than one foot to a few thousand feet. The type
section is a composite affair, built up by combining well
developed sections found in widely scattered areas of the
earth." And T. H. Huxley states, "All that geology can
prove is a local order of succession. . . . Devonian fauna and
flora in the British Isles may have been contemporaneous
with Silurian life in North America and with carboniferous
fauna and flora in Africa. . . . Geographical provinces and
zones may have been as distinctly marked in the Palaeozoic
epoch as at present".

It is also interesting to note that the order of the strata is not the same in all places where they are found lying one above another. Professor S. J. Bole says that "one of the questions that the evolutionary geologist cannot answer is that of *the upside down condition* of rocks found far and wide". Such upside down areas are seen in China, Norway, the Alps, Scotland, New York, Tennessee, Georgia, and other places. Where such anomalous and embarrassing situations arose, the evolutionist had always an explanation that some cataclysm has occurred – the earth had an upthrust fold and therefore showed the fossils in a different order. Thus, to quote McReady Price, "even over areas covering thousands of square miles where the strata lie in a perfectly normal sequence, showing no sign of cataclysm or fold, the evolutionist would blame old Mother Earth and reckon it as her 'fault' rather than admit that there was something wrong with his geological column".

The geological column seems to be a faked one; for the fossils are first arranged according to the strata in which they are found and the strata are then arranged according to the fossils found in them. Often when fossils are found in unwelcome strata either their names are changed or the date of the rock in which the fossils appeared is changed. For example when *Equus* was found in India in the miocene rocks (older than those which contained their ancestors), they were altered to pliocene first, and then to pleistocene, in order to show the pedigree of the horse. Thus Grabau in *Principles of Stratigraphy*, p. 1103, says: "The primary divisions of the geological time scale are, as we have seen, based on the changes in life, with the result that *fossils alone determine whether* a formation belongs to one or other of these great divisions." That the character of the strata is of no consideration is evident from the following quotation from H. S. Williams in his *Geological Biology*, pp. 37, 38. He writes: "These systems, although actually arbitrary groupings of the stratified rocks of particular regions, have come into common use as the primary divisions of the rocks whenever chronological sequence is considered. In describing any newly discovered fossiliferous strata in any part of the earth, the first step to be taken in giving them a scientific definition is to assign them to one or other of the systems upon evidence of the fossils found in them. The character of the rocks themselves, their composition or their mineral content, have nothing to do with settling the question as to the particular system to which the new rocks belong. *The fossils alone are the means of correlation.*"

The geological column, therefore, is an artificial composite affair with the strata arbitrarily arranged according to the nature of their fossil content to tell the story of evolution. As Dr. Frank Marsh puts it: "There is no spot on earth to which one can go and see more than a few thousand vertical feet of stratified rocks. And in none of these places can the evolutionary story of any animal or plant be seen" – *Evolution, Creation and Science*, p. 221.

The facts of palaeontology seem to support creation and the Flood rather than evolution. For instance, *all the major groups of invertebrates appear "suddenly"* in the first fossiliferous strata (Cambrian) of the earth with their distinct specialisations, indicating that they were all created almost at the same time. *Cambrian Strata* not only holds all the fossils of invertebrate phyla, but even vertebrate phyla. A sandled human footprint with Trilobite fossils in it was recently discovered (1968) in *Cambrian Strata* at Antelope Springs, Utah, U.S.A.[1] Compare the human skeleton recently unearthed from cretaceous rocks in Utah province near Moab.[2] *Palynology:* "In the last fifteen years spores of vascular plants have been reported from the cambrian. Axelrod reports that over 60 cambrian spore genera are now on record. Leclerq believes the finding of spores of woody plants already in the cambrian raised the question of the phylactic origin of vascular plants. This is another way of saying that, as far back as we can trace geologically, *plants are as distinct from one another as now. This certainly is strong evidence for an original creation of them as distinctive kinds.*"[3]

In an article entitled "Living fossil plants a challenge to evolution" in *Science Reporter* published by Scientific and Industrial Research, Rafi Marg, New Delhi, p. 21 (January, 1974) by Shri Sharma and Shri Singh (botanists), it is said,

Cibotium tasmanense: "These living fossils as they are called, pose a serious question to the very basis of the theory of evolution." R. E. Gould (1972) of Yale University after studying Cibotium tasmanense, is of the opinion that living Cibotium is nearly the same as the ancient Cibotium tasmanense which supposedly lived over 200 million years ago and fossilised in the rocks at the end of tertiary period.

Equisetum: This is another living fossil of today.

Gymnosperms: Among gymnosperms, cycads are practically unchanged and still exist in much the same form as they lived 200 million years ago.

Angiosperms: Among angiosperms, the Sequois tree has remained unchanged from its fossil forms said to be over 200 million years old.

Why are these fossil plants unchanged? Evolutionists have no answer. Indeed living fossils throw a challenge to scientists and laymen alike to look again at the theory of evolution. Can it be because the theory of evolution is a scientific mistake? Or can it be that the age of the earth is not as old as it is often believed to be?

These refute the assumption of the evolutionists that any group evolved from any other group through a long interval of time, or that one phylum is any older than any other phylum. Again the upside down order of earth's strata, in many parts of the globe, contradicts the evolutionary order of fossils.

HOW WERE THE FOSSILS FORMED?

The occurrence of fossils in great numbers aggregated together and showing marks of violence as the mammoths in Siberia, suggests that they were entombed suddenly in a flood as Sir Henry Haworth in *The Mammoth and Flood* describes. Hugh Miller in the *Old Red Sandstones*, p. 221,

says that "over an area of more than 10,000 square miles
fish remains are found bearing unequivocally marks of
violent death. The figures are contorted, contracted, curved;
the tail in many cases is bent around to the head, the spines
stick out, the fins are spread to the full". Further information
of the sudden entombment of animals may be read from
W. Buclands *Geology and Mineralogy*, Vol. 1, p. 24. Describing the petrified fishes of the Alps, the author states, "They
are always entire, and so closely packed one on another that
many individuals are often contained in a single block. All
these fish must have died suddenly on this fatal spot, and
have been buried speedily in the sediment then in course of
deposition. From the fact that certain individuals have been
preserved with traces of colour upon their skin, we are
certain that they were entombed before decomposition of
their soft parts had taken place". The so-called Devonian
rocks have abundant remains of sharks which died in the
natural swimming position, with their backs slightly
flattened by the weight of mud that settled upon them. Sir
Henry Haworth, who was hostile to the Bible, describing
the mammoths entombed in icy muck in Siberia writes that
"nothing but a sudden flood can account for conditions as
they exist". Such a burial in herds indicated a catastrophe
like the Deluge described in the Bible. Further proof is
scientifically documented in *The Genesis Flood* by doctors
Henry M. Morris and John C. Whitcomb (1962).

The writer of this book himself visited Princeton University in 1963 to examine a rectangular block about three feet
in length, containing the fossil remains of three rhinoceros.
To him it seems that all the phenomena of the fossils described above, and all the other facts of geology and palaen-
tology, can reasonably be explained only in terms of the
Deluge described in the Bible. Other irrefutable arguments
for a catastrophic flood or deluge are based on observed facts
pointed out by Cuvier, namely the existence of land animals
found buried under marine productions. The preservation of
shells with minute details and soft animals shows that

they were covered quickly and not by slow wave action.[4] A corrupted version of the flood account is found in many records of the ancients. In the beginning there was created a world of beauty with luxuriant vegetation, teeming with a greater variety of animals than at present. Then a vast catastrophe buried them all in mud, preserving animals and plants at different levels of strata in different parts of the earth. This view is further supported by two scientific facts that have come to light recently.

(1) Most of the earth's surface is covered with sediments or sedimentary rocks, originally deposited under moving water. This in itself is a *prima facie* evidence that powerful waters once covered the earth.

(2) The discovery of "Polystrata fossils" or large fossils of animals and plants especially tree trunks that are found extending through several strata, often 20 feet or more in thickness. This type of fossil must have been buried quickly or it would not have been preserved intact while the strata gradually accumulated around it.[5]

These may not answer all the questions of the Bible student. But as far as the facts of Palaeontology are concerned, the Bible answer seems to be a far better explanation than that offered by the theory of evolution. Fossil evidence, or evidence from historical biology, seems to be more in favour of creation than evolution.

[1] C.R.S. Quarterly 1968, Vol. 5, No. 3, page 97.
[2] C.R.S. 1973, Vol. 10, No. 2, page 109.
[3] See C.R.S. Quarterly December 1968, Vol. 5, No. 3 and page 103. Wilbert Rusch, Sr.
[4] See C.R.S. 1965, Vol. 2, No. 1, page 51 on Cuvier.
[5] See Henry M. Morris – "*Sedimentation and the fossil record*" – C.R.S. 1967, Vol. 4, No. 3, page 95.

Chapter 3

THE AGE OF THE EARTH

A question that naturally arises in one's mind at this juncture is: How old is the earth? How old are the various strata and the fossils which they contain? Is there any scientific method of determining these? It is difficult to explain the various ways in which the age of the earth's strata and fossils are determined. However, it may be stated in brief that there is no scientific way of determining their age exactly or even approximately *without making certain basic assumptions*. Whether it be the sedimentary system of dating or the radioactive system, it is assumed that sedimentation of rocks and radioactive disintegration of minerals have gone on at a uniform rate throughout the history of the earth. This is a tremendous assumption, and is not supported by the facts. There is evidence even now that sedimentation does not take place at the same rate at different points of the earth. Rate of sedimentation varies according to different conditions. For the stalactite growth may be more rapid than postulated. A dam in Oregon built in 1890 and abandoned in 1912 had on the spill way ceilings, stalactites from 18-20 mm. in length, as reported in C.R.S. 1971, Vol. 8, No. 3, p. 188. Another instance is cited from Old Fort Pickens constructed 140 years ago where stalactites are found to be 13-14 inches long.[1]

This information could substantially affect the time span of the geological column and contribute to the ever-growing volume of evidence for a recent scriptural creation. For example, it was found that a pair of gloves left in a dripping well at Knaresborough in Yorkshire turned into stone in a few days, because of the rapid rate of deposition. On the other hand, there are areas where it takes hundreds of years to effect such sedimentation.

The same may be said about the radio-active system of age determination. According to Dr. Marsh, uranium with atomic weight 238 disintegrates by successive *alpha* and *beta* particle emissions passing through thirteen intermediary products until it finally becomes lead, which is stable with atomic weight 206. Physical chemists estimate a period of 4,600,000,000 years to change half the uranium in a mineral into lead. From this, the time taken for uranium to become residue lead can be calculated in any sample of rock. Though the uranium-lead method looks so simple, hazards are many, as radio-active series are often found to be in disequilibrium. This apart, there is no means of knowing whether all the lead found in a sample of rock is radiogenic or not. It may be primordial lead which has the same atomic weight as residual (radiogenic) lead. These two cannot be distinguished from one another even by chemical analysis. Radiogenic lead may be mixed with primordial lead. For the same Creator who made the mother element could have created also the daughter elements at the same time. According to Henry Paul's *Nuclear Geology*, p. 297, in a uranium mineral the lead is in part primordial and in part radiogenic. And so long as there is no means of determining how much of each is present in a mineral, there will be uncertainty in every age determination.

RADIO-CARBON METHOD

A more popular and recent method of dating is known as the carbon 14 or (radio carbon) method. Radio carbon is formed when protons of cosmic radiation collide with nitrogen atoms of our atmosphere, thus releasing neutrons. This free neutron on entering another atom of nitrogen thrusts out one of its protons, converting the nitrogen atom $7N^{14}$ to $6C^{14}$ or *radio carbon* or carbon 14, having an atomic weight of 14 instead of 12. As soon as this radio carbon or C^{14} is formed it combines with O_2 of the atmosphere forming CO_2. This CO_2 is readily absorbed by green plants during assimilation forming sugar, etc. Living things absorb this radio carbon as fast as they lose it in their wastes. As soon as an organism dies the total radio carbon begins to lessen. Thus the older the organic material the less the radio carbon left in it. In this manner the rate of loss due to disintegration immediately after death is calculated to be 15.3 disintegrations per minute per gram which can be measured by means of a Geiger Counter. The rate decreases as the years pass by and the amount of C^{14} left in the material also becomes less correspondingly. It is found that at the end of 5,566 years, half the radio carbon disappears. Samples of known age up to 4,500 years have given fairly accurate readings. But beyond this span of historic time, dating is highly unreliable by this method.

Evolutionists take it for granted that cosmic radiation was uniform throughout the earth's span of life. This is an assumption not accepted by the scientists who are creationists. The latter affirm that cosmic radiation was *not* uniform throughout, but that it suddenly increased when the water vapour in the firmament enveloping the earth collapsed during the Noachian flood. According to creationists such a catastrophic change in the world's climate is evidenced by the refrigerated mammoths and the sub-tropical vegetation buried suddenly in ice in the Arctic regions. They also affirm that the proportion of CO_2 in the air was at least ten times that of today, because of the luxuriant vegetation that existed then. For these and other reasons Professor Arthur Holmes, who did much work in dating the earth, admitted the following in his *Physics of the Earth*, p. 11: "The only assumption that can reasonably be called in question is that of *uniformity* and it is involved equally in both calculations (i.e. sedimentary and radioactive systems)." James R. Arnold in his book *Nuclear Geology* (1954), p. 350, says: "So far there is no proof independent of the method, that the cosmic ray intensity has remained constant, and however reasonable it may be, we must rank this as a pure assumption." This apart, the formation of radio carbon was shown to be reduced during the industrial revolution, and during volcanic eruptions, since these increased the amount of CO_2 in the atmosphere. It may also be said that the weakening of the earth's magnetic field for the last 2,000 years has had a check on cosmic rays.

These facts show how unreliable the radio carbon datings can be, and consequently how fossils can appear to be much older than they actually are. Moreover, if creationist scientists are right in maintaining that the water vapour envelope, which existed at the time of Noah, fell on the earth during the Noachian flood, then cosmic radiation as we know it, would only begin at this time. This would reduce the geological ages of millions of years into practically nothing.

Thus to the question how old is the earth or how old is a particular fossil, no reliable scientific answer can be given. *There is no dependable method of dating which can scientifically prove the correct or even approximate age of rock more than 4,000 to 5,000 years old!* The dating of fossils too seems to be arbitrary. Dr. H. C. Morton relates a case in which American scientists had to reduce the age of a skeleton found in the Mississippi from 50,000 years to 5,000 on finding a modern flat-bottomed boat below this skeleton. Other instances of changing dates can be cited. It may therefore be stated that neither the geological column nor the chronological time scale fixed on it can be scientifically accurate.

[1] See C.R.S. 1973, Vol. 10, No. 2, page 130.

Chapter 4

THE AGE OF THE EARTH
AND OF THE UNIVERSE

In 1964 a man was charged in court with stealing from Wookey Hole Caves, Somerset, England, a stalagmite declared by experts to be 42,000 years old. On what was this estimate based? Upon the well-known fact that sedimentation as observed today occurs at a fixed rate. Therefore if a stalagmite is 42 inches high, and the known rate of deposit one tenth of an inch in 100 years, obviously its age is 42,000 years *if there was nothing there to begin with*.

But is it not possible that God might have created the earth with caves, stalactites, stalagmites and all from the very beginning? Is it not possible that when God created the earth He made this particular stalagmite 36 inches high, so that its actual age is only 6,000 years, though its *apparent* age is 42,000? Recent discoveries show that stalactites and stalagmites can be formed rapidly and that evolutionists are in great error to assert that stalactite and stalagmite accretion requires multiple thousands of years. Evidently a stalagmite occurs so rapidly that a bat can be entombed before actions of bacterial decay or predators![1]

In the case of Adam and Eve it is quite certain that God created them full-grown, with the power to cultivate a garden, to name and tame the animals, and to procreate children. But a modern physiologist meeting Adam in the garden of Eden would say to himself: "This man must be at least twenty years old. He has all the bodily functions which, as I have observed them, require twenty years of development from infancy." The physiologist would be wrong! Why? Because he fails to take account of the fact of CREATION, which is something entirely beyond a physiologist's experience. On the first Sabbath day Adam and Eve had an *apparent* age of say, twenty, but an *actual* age of only one day. In exactly similar fashion a stalagmite today may have an actual age of 6,000 years when its apparent age is very much greater.

The same reasoning may be applied to every part of the Universe. The latest estimate of its age according to Dr. Sandage of Mount Palomar, California (as quoted in the *Times* of 13th January, 1965), is 12,000 million years. This figure is based partly on the speed of light and the distance from us of the farthest stars. But of course the great God who made the stars out of nothing could equally well cause their light to fall on the earth at the moment of creation. He who "speeded up" the formation of Adam and Eve, compressing the work of twenty years into one second, could equally well have increased the speed of light to any degree He chose.

The age of the Universe is also calculated by comparing the combustion rate of the stars with their mass. To determine how long a torch has been shining all I need to know is (a) the rate of consumption, (b) the amount of electrical energy remaining in the battery. Suppose the "life" of a battery to be two hours, and I find it is half run down, I infer that the torch has been shining for one hour. But suppose the battery was not brand new when inserted in the torch! Then it will be absolutely impossible to calculate how long it has been shining. Just so God created Adam not "brand new" (as a baby), but as a full-grown man; and He created the stars with an *apparent* age (slightly run down) quite different from their real age. So the apparent age of our sun, 5,000 million years, can in no way affect the Bible declaration that God made it on the fourth day, *after* the earth, and only two days before the first human being.

Again, one method of computing the age of the earth is by the salinity of the oceans. We quote from George Gamow's book, *The Creation of the Universe* (1952): Dividing the known total amount of salt at present dissolved in the oceans by the known amount of salt brought in yearly by rivers, we find that the salinity of the oceans increases by one millionth of one per cent each century. . . . It follows that the rivers must have been at work for about 300 million years for the present amount of oceanic salts (three per cent) to have accumulated.

Arithmetic – excellent! but logic – poor. Why should the Creator not have made the sea salt from the beginning? On the third day "God said, Let the waters under the heaven be gathered together unto one place, and let the dry land appear: and it was so". And written on stone by the finger of God were these words: "In six days the Lord made heaven and earth, the sea, and all that in them is" – including the salt!

The cardinal error of modern scientists who reject the Genesis record of creation – whether astronomers, geologists, physicists, chemists, or biologists – is their UNIFORMITARIANISM, i.e., belief that physical causes and effects in all ages have been only and always the same as those which we observe today. This error was foreseen by God and foretold in the Bible: "In the last days mockers shall come, saying, Where is the promise of Christ's coming? for *all things continue as they were from the beginning of the creation.*" The writer goes on to say that these unbelievers wilfully forget the fact of the universal Flood, which broke all the laws of Uniformity in the not-so-distant past.

POPULAR FALLACIES

A common fallacy today is to think that Genesis was written for simple-minded primitive people in terms which they could readily understand, and that it is only this modern "scientific" age that has found difficulty in accepting the account at its face value. In fact one of the greatest "difficulties" lies on the very surface of the narrative: it boldly narrates that three days and nights passed before the creation of the Sun, which even the most ignorant savage can see is the cause of our evenings and mornings. Calvin's comment on this passage is worth quoting: "It did not happen from inconsideration or by accident, that the light preceded the sun and the moon. To nothing are we more prone than to tie down the power of God to those instruments, the agency of which He employs. The sun and moon supply us with light: and, according to our notions, we so include this power to give light in them, that if they were taken away from the world, it would seem impossible for any light to remain. Therefore the Lord, by the very order of the Creation, bears witness that He holds in His hand the light, which He is able to impart to us without the sun and moon."

So far from Creation being a "primitive" idea, the fact is that even Plato and Aristotle, the most brilliant European philosophers of antiquity, could not conceive of a time when the world did not exist, but thought it must have been eternal. The doctrine of Evolution, on the other hand, is as old as the hills, and can be found in varying forms among the most primitive tribes today. Nowhere in all ancient literature, except in the Bible, is the idea of Creation *ex nihilo* set forth. This surely indicates that whereas the doctrine of Evolution is a product of man's unaided reasoning, the doctrine of Creation is a product of God's unique revelation.

Another popular fallacy is that the date 4004 B.C. which is found at the head of the book of Genesis in older editions of the English Bible, may safely be disregarded because it was worked out by a 17th century Archbishop named Ussher who obviously knew very little science. It is not so well known that Sir Isaac Newton, who is generally acknowledged as the world's greatest man of science, after independent calculations based on the Bible's chronology *agreed with Ussher's date for the Creation and saw nothing in astronomy to cause him to doubt it*! No discovery of the last three centuries has altered by one whit the essential facts of the case. The real difference between Isaac Newton and Fred Hoyle is not the difference between little knowledge and more knowledge, but between faith in God's revelation, on the one hand, and disbelief on the other. Every Christian readily admits that God *could* have taken billions of years to form the earth, and billions more to form man. But He *says* that He *didn't*: "For *in six days* the Lord made heaven and earth, the sea, and all that in them is."[2] And to the unbelieving His question is still unanswerable:

"Where wast thou when I laid the foundations of the earth? . . . Doubtless thou knowest, for thou wast then born, and the number of thy days is great!" (Job. 38: 4, 21).

But the one who has come to trust in Jesus for the salvation of his soul will be content to rest in the revelation of Jesus for his mind; knowing that all oppositions of science, if such there are, will be oppositions of "science *falsely so called*" (1 Timothy 6: 20).

---

[1] See cover illustration, C.R.S. Quarterly, Vol. 8, No. 2, September 1971.
[2] See also Chapter 17.

Chapter 5

THE NATURE OF THE FOSSILS
ON EARTH'S STRATA

Assuming the geological column and the time scale fixed by evolutionists to be true, we may now examine the nature of the fossils contained in them. Dr. Merson Davis, D.SC., PH.D., a careful student of geology, challenges Professor Julian Huxley's hypothesis of slow evolution through geological periods of time in his article *The Science of Dr. Julian Huxley* published in *The English Churchman* in August 1951. "The geological facts flatly oppose it (evolution). For all the great groups of creatures, and all the most highly specialised types, appear suddenly and in full efficiency from the first, there being *no links* between the *phyla*, classes or even orders. In other words, links are entirely missing just where on the Darwinian theory, they should be most numerous. . . . The new structures which appear so often exhibit intricate correlations of different parts, which will be useless until complete; so natural selection itself would have eliminated intermediate forms instead of preserving them." This is admitted by H. H. Newmann in his book on *Evolution, Genetics and Eugenics* under principal fact No. 3. "The animals and plants of the oldest geological strata represent all existing *phyla* except the *chordata*, but the representatives of the various *phyla* are relatively generalised as compared with existing types." As against the latter statement Dr. D. H. Scott, one of the greatest authorities on fossil botany, in his *Extinct Plant and*

Problems of Evolution, p. 147, writes: "The average level of the Lycopods of the Carboniferous Age was altogether far higher than that of the same group in our own time." And again: "Some of the most complicated seeds known are of Palaeozoic Age . . . subsequent changes have been on the whole in the direction of simplification" (p. 169). The old argument that they could not be fossilised in these crystalline rocks does not hold water. For as Professor McReady Price would suggest: "The condition of a rock as to its degree of solidification or crystallisation is no guarantee as to the kinds of fossil which it may contain. Any type of life, even what used to be called the very youngest, is likely to be found in crystalline or metamorphic rock, as old in appearance as any on the globe." Again, Newmann in his fact No. 10 says: "Most of the invertebrate *phyla* had already undergone more than half their evolution at the time when the earliest fossil remains were deposited." This seems to be only an apology for the sudden appearance of most of the invertebrate groups (and some fish skeletons, according to Dunbar) with their distinct specialisations. There is no indication whatever that they slowly evolved from a bit of protoplasm, as the proponents of evolution would expect. Professor A. H. Cook (*Cambridge Natural History*, vol III, p. 5), says: "The first undisputed traces of life which appear in the Cambrian epoch exhibit the same phyletic distinctions as now exist. Sponges, echinoderms, molluscs and worms formed already in these immeasurable remote ages, are groups apparently as generally distinct from one another as they are at the present time. The fact is, there is no fossil evidence for the evolution of invertebrates; they all appear suddenly, and fully specialised."

Yet in his fact No. 5 Newmann states: "There is in general a gradual progression towards higher types as one proceeds from the lower to the higher strata." But Charles Darwin (*Origin of Species*, Vol. II, p. 49), stated: "Geology assuredly does not reveal any such finely graded organic chain; and this is perhaps the most obvious and serious

objection that can be urged against the theory of evolution."
And one hundred years of research since Darwin's time has
in no way weakened the validity of this objection.

Again in the ninth principal fact of Newmann it is stated:
"The evolution of the vertebrate classes is more satisfactorily shown than that of any other group, probably
because they represent the last *phyla* to evolve and most
of their history coincides with the period within which
fossils are known." Professor Newmann is here probably
referring to the pedigrees of the horse, camel and elephant,
exhibited as proofs of evolution in the Natural History
Museum of New York. A look at these series, especially the
pedigree of the horse, seems quite convincing to a casual
observer. If only the fossil horses were found in the order in
which they are arranged in successively younger strata
according to the law of superposition, then there would be
some sense in assuming that the modern horse had evolved
out of forms like Eohippus. But the facts are otherwise.
The bones of the pedigree horses were gathered from
different parts of the world and arranged in evolutionary
sequence. In no one place on earth can these "ancestors" of
the horse be found in this order of evolutionary sequence.
In fact it is equally reasonable to assume that they all existed
on earth at the same time. *The only reason for arranging the
fossils in this order* from the "Dawn Horse" (Eohippus) to
the modern horse, is the assumption that evolution has taken
place. Thus after artificially arranging the fossils to tell the
story of evolution, evolutionists turn round and offer the
same as proof of evolution! It is this that made Charles
Duperett – one of the greatest of French Palaeontologists –
call this particular kind of proof "a *deceitful delusion*" (see
Transformations of the Animal World, p. 105).

Here again, the same objection of T. H. Morgan against
the proof from classification holds good. Yet, sad to say,
not only professors and students of Universities but even
the general public are deceived by such artificial arrangements of these fossils in the great museums, and by the

photographs of casts published in text books of geology.

It may not be out of place to relate a recent experience of the author in Ceylon, while debating the theory of evolution with the University students. One of the Professors (a Ph.D.) who opposed him held out the pedigree of the horse as an irrefutable proof of evolution. Like many other Professors he was under the mistaken idea that these fossils were dug out in successive layers, as arranged in the New York Museum. He was not aware of the fact that a hoof of the modern horse was discovered in Colorado in older strata than the bones of Eohippus. Such ignorance of the real facts concerning the pedigree of the horse, even among Professors, is not surprising. For often facts opposed to the theory of evolution are not published in text books. Sometimes they are deliberately withheld. Notwithstanding, even if the pedigree of the horse or the camel or the elephant could be demonstrated in the rocks it would only show variation within the "kind" mentioned in the Bible. The connecting links between the basic "kinds" mentioned in Genesis would be entirely lacking. This lack of connecting links between the "kinds" is a very serious objection to the theory of evolution, as Darwin himself has stated in his *Origin of Species* – already quoted.

There are a number of animals of peculiar forms existing today, sharply marked off from others. If these are the modified descendents of generalised forms, as evolutionists hold, then each must have a line of ancestors intermediate in form between it and the generalised ancestor. But, as pointed out by the late Mr. Douglas Dewar, the fossils discovered so far do not show even a single species of animal intermediate in form between the generalised ancestor and the modern sharply differentiated forms. For example, evolutionists believe that whales have descended from land animals by a series of modifications in successive generations. It is estimated that at least thirty intermediate links might have been necessary for the terrestrial mammal to become a whale. But the study of fossils has discovered not even a single link on the rocks to this day. The same may be said of seals, which are supposed to have had at least eight intermediate links from land mammals and the bats about twenty from wingless mammals.

So, the complete absence of such links on the rocks renders it almost certain that such intermediate forms have never existed. By T. H. Huxley's criterion: "If evolution has taken place, there (on the rocks) will its mark be left: if it has not taken place, there will be its refutation" – by that criterion, evolution has never taken place in the past.

INTERMEDIATE FOSSILS

It is often published in text books that *Archaeopteryx* links reptiles and birds and *Ictidosauria* links reptiles and mammals and *Ichthyostegus* links fishes and amphibia. But a more detailed study of these so-called intermediary fossils reveals that every fossil cited as intermediate between two classes, belongs to one or other of the two classes. Thus *Archaeopteryx* is a toothed bird like any other cretaceous bird, having well developed feathers and warm blood. The theory that feathers are frayed out scales, can no longer be maintained, as they do not even arise from the same layer of epidermis as the scales.

Ictidosauria are true reptiles sharply marked off from mammals by the presence of a single columella instead of the three ear ossicles of mammals; by the indirect articulation of the lower jaw of many bones by means of a quadrate, instead of the direct articulation of the single bone in mammals. However, it is true that adaptive radiation did produce a number of "mammal-like reptiles", just as the Australian marsupials produced a number of varieties which looked like the placental mammals. *Ichthyostegus*, again, is undoubtedly an amphibian, in spite of its resemblance to a fish in certain minor characteristics. Often it is affirmed in text books written by evolutionists that there is "an unbroken transition from the reptilian to the mammalian plan of structure". But there are no fossils showing any transitions from the reptilian lower jaw and inner ear to the lower jaw and inner ear of a mammal. Such a transition is even unthinkable, since such intermediate forms would neither be able to eat, or hear during the long period of transition. Similarly man could not have evolved from monkeys or apes as all the living animals are too specialised to have given rise to so generalised a structure as man's. All the so-called missing links that have been "cooked up" in the past have disappeared one by one, as our knowledge of ancient men that lived on this globe has increased.

Dr. Henry Fairfield Osborne, former curator of the American Museum of Natural History, who had the privilege of examining more skulls than any contemporary scientist, states: "I regard the ape-human theory as totally false and misleading. It should be banished from our speculation and our literature, not on sentimental grounds but on purely scientific grounds, and we should now resolutely set our faces towards the discovery of our actual pre-human ancestors." The fact is, there are no fossils recorded on the rocks linking one *phylum* with another or one basic "kind" with another basic kind. And the categorical and unambiguous statements of that prince among palaeontologists, Louis Agassiz of Harvard University, are as true today as they were in the days of Charles Darwin. He said in his book *Methods of Study in Natural History*, "As a palaeontologist I have from the beginning stood aloof from this new theory of transmutation (evolution) of species now so widely admitted by the scientific world. Its doctrines in fact contradict what the animal forms buried in the rock strata of the earth tell us of their own introduction and succession on the surface of the globe. The theory is a scientific mistake. . . . There is not a fact known in science tending to show that any being in the natural process of reproduction and multiplication has ever diverged from the course natural to its kind or that a single kind has ever been transmuted (evolved) into any other".

George Gaylord Simpson, palaeontologist of Columbia University, in his book *Tempo and Mode of Evolution* (1944), writes on page 115: "As it became more and more evident that the great gaps remained despite wonderful progress in finding the members of lower transitional groups and progressive lines, it was no longer satisfactory to impute their absence of objective data entirely to chance. The failure of Palaeontology to produce such evidence was so keenly felt that a few disillusioned naturalists even decided that the theory of organic continuity of descent was wrong after all." On page 7 of his book *An Introduction to Palaeontology* (1947) Chester A. Arnold, Professor of Botany, University of Michigan, writes: "As yet we have not been able to trace the phylogenetic history of a single group of modern plants from its beginning to the present." Later, in 1953, G. G. Simpson wrote (*The Major Feature of Evolution*, p. 360): "In spite of these examples, it remains true, as every palaeontologist knows, that most new species, genera and families appear in the record suddenly and are not led up to by known gradual, completely continuous transitional sequences." D. Dwight Davis, curator of the Natural History Museum, Chicago, in his book, *Genetics, Palaeontology and Evolution* (1949), on pages 74 and 77 writes (as quoted by Dr. Frank Marsh): "The sudden emergence of major adaptive types as seen in the abrupt appearance in the fossil record of families and orders, continued to give trouble. The phenomenon lay in the genetical no-man's-land beyond the limits of experimentation. A few palaeontologists even today cling to the idea that these gaps will be closed by further collecting, i.e. they are accidents of sampling; but most regard the observed discontinuities as real and have sought an explanation for them." "But the facts of Palaeontology conform equally well with other interpretations that have been discredited by neo-biological work, e.g. divine creation, innate developmental processes, Lamarckism, etc., and palaeontology by itself can neither prove nor refute such ideas." The same author on page 14 quotes Dr. A. S. Romer of Harvard University, "The chances of obtaining a complete graded series (if one existed) are hence obviously vastly less than in the case of more normal phyletic evolution. 'Links' are missing just where we most fervently desire them, and it is all too probable that many 'links' will continue to be missing."

It may therefore be asserted that the facts of Palaeontology, namely, the sudden appearance of all the invertebrates with their distinct specialisation in the Cambrian Era, and the complete absence of "undisputed" fossils in the pre-cambrian rocks, and the absence of intermediate forms linking the basic kinds of animals and plants, argue more for instantaneous creation than for evolution.

Chapter 6

EVIDENCES FROM EMBRYOLOGY

Of late this has lost its importance, and evolutionists themselves view it with suspicion; but as it is still published in text books it is worth while examining it.

It is claimed by some zoologists that during the development of an organism from a single cell to the adult form, there is a recapitulation of its racial history. Thus a fertilised human egg passes through a many-celled stage comparable to a protozoan colony, a fish stage, a reptile stage, and a monkey or chimpanzee stage, till it finds its completion in the highest form – Man. In other words the embryological development of man is nothing but a moving picture of 500 million years of human history: or *ontogeny* (life-history of the individual) is a recapitulation of *phylogeny* (racial history). This theory was first formulated by Haeckel of Germany, himself by no means a specialist in embryology, who based it upon the superficial resemblances between mammal embryos noticed by Von Baer. The latter actually studied the embryos, but never believed in evolution to the end of his life. Haeckel, however, found the idea so fascinating that he called it "the fundamental law of Biogenesis". It caught the imagination of many embryologists, and much research was done in that direction: but the research only showed that, though there was vague similarity in the development of all embryos, Haeckel's interpretation of the facts was simply wishful thinking. Professor Sedgwick, an embryologist, stated that "fifty years of research and close examination of the facts of embryology has left the recapitulation theory without satisfactory proofs".

Professor Locy, an evolutionist, says in his book *Biology and its Makers* (p. 230), that in development "many stages have been dropped out, others are unduly prolonged or abbreviated, or appear out of their chronological order. Some of the structures have arisen from adaptation, and are not therefore ancestral at all. The interpretation becomes a difficult task, and requires much balance of judgment and profound analysis."

T. H. Morgan, himself an evolutionist, in his *Critique of the Theory of Evolution* cites several instances of embryonic forms which cannot represent ancestral animals. An obvious one is the embryo chick in its shell. "Hundreds of such cases are known to embryologists, and are explained as falsification of the ancestral records" (I. c.p. 17). This is the kind of proof offered by evolutionists. The reader will remember how in a previous chapter under "Palaeontological Evidence" mother earth was at "fault" whenever she did not show the fossils in the order demanded by the evolutionists. And now a "balanced judgment and profound analysis" apparently leads us to conclude that it is nature, not the evolutionist, who has falsified the facts of history!

Until the beginning of this century the recapitulation theory had a good following all over the world, but the intensive research carried out of late has considerably lessened its importance, and today it is largely abandoned by evolutionists. Thus Professor E. B. Wilson, Dean of American Embryologists, states: "There is a strong suspicion that the embryological record has somehow failed, and there are even some embryologists who seem to be almost ready to abandon the recapitulation theory." Professor T. S. Westoll called it "sheer nonsense". But in spite of the categorical rejection of the theory by men of great scientific status, and distinguished embryologists, there are still a few teachers of Biology who obstinately cling to it. While admitting that the majority of embryonic stages have no ancestral significance, they still maintain the doctrine in regard to a few stages. We shall now consider some of these.

(1) *The Fish Stage.* It is contended by evolutionists that the embryos of high vertebrates like men, pigs, cats, birds, etc., have gill-slits at an early stage of their development, and these gill-slits are relics of the past when man was a fish. But Sir Arthur Keith states that "at no stage in the higher embryo is the wall of the alimentary canal perforated". Gray's *Anatomy*, 15th edition, page 1168, states, "In gill-bearing animals the grooves become complete clefts, the gill-clefts opening from pharynx to the interior; perforation does not occur, however, in birds and mammals".

Keith called the "gills" *furrows* and Ballantyne called them *grooves.* In aquatic animals they give rise to gills and gill-slits, but in higher animals they become ear cavities, lower jaw and neck parts. Thus the resemblance between the two groups is only superficial and transient, up to the stage of the folds: thereafter the development of each is along entirely different lines.

Douglas Dewar, an Ornithologist, in his book *Difficulties of Evolution Theory*, page 49, says: "In the embryo of a reptile, bird or mammal (including man), no cleft forms between the arches, which never assume the characteristics of gills. It is clearly incorrect to call them gill arches. The embryo of a higher animal never passes through a fish stage." Again, "Embryology lends no countenance to the view that the higher vertebrates evolved from a fish-like ancestor. It is only by putting far-fetched and artificial interpretations on embryological phenomena that they can be made to fit in with the evolution hypothesis".

(2) *The Monkey Stage.* It is further claimed that when the embryo of man is of the size of a pea it passes through a "tailed" stage. Here again a critical examination reveals that the "tail" of a human embryo is in no way comparable to

the tail of a lower animal, for the intestine extends into this "tail" – a phenomenon which has no parallel in any tailed vertebrate.

The so-called tail is only the coccyx or the end of the vertebral column. On further growth the coccyx is covered with muscles, etc., which are very useful. In any case the presence of a tail cannot be offered as a proof of man's descent from a tailed vertebrate, since some of the vertebrates in the evolutionary ladder possess no tail.

Professor A. Richards in his *Outlines of Comparative Anatomy* (1951), pages 291-294, states: " . . . the facts do not at all fit into the biogenetic interpretation. . . . In many cases the actual order of development is the reverse of what would be demanded by recapitulation. For example, in the evolution of mammals, teeth are supposed to have developed before the tongue; but in the embryo the tongue appears before teeth." Further, in his *Human Body* (p. 95) Keith says, "the human body is at no stage anthropoid in its appearance". However we may admit resemblances without conceding that they prove anything in regard to evolution or recapitulation. All animals start life as a single cell, less than 1/100th of an inch in diameter. To the human eye, therefore, they must necessarily resemble each other in the egg stage and through many of the earlier states, until each begins to diverge according to its own peculiarity. These peculiarities always existed though invisible even through the microscope. Thus the apparent resemblance is due to our defective means of examination; but to claim genetic relationship because of it, ignoring the vast differences of later development, is quite unwarranted and illogical. The recapitulation theory at best is only an assumption and not a proof.

THE RECAPITULATION THEORY SELF-DESTRUCTIVE

Granting that the theory of recapitulation is right, and a force called Natural Selection operates to change one type of animal into another, then that force aims at improving not only the form of the animal but also its methods of development. Natural Selection not being a conservative agent, should get rid of all ancestral methods of development which are of no use to its descendant. Natural Selection cannot be expected to preserve these ancestral methods unless they are essential for the development of the descendants also. And if these methods are necessary for the proper development of the descendant, they are likely to be acquired afresh even if they are not ancestral. The fact is, as our knowledge of embryology progresses it is increasingly clear that every process in the development of an embryo is essential for its development at one stage or another. As in the case of "vestigial organs", Nature preserves no organ or method of development just to indicate the ancestry of an animal. As Dr. Merson Davies further points out: "The forces which have entirely removed the supposedly most recent anthropoid foot from man's embryology, presumably because it was no longer wanted there, could hardly have allowed such vastly older features (like 'gill-slits' and 'tails') to remain, unless they were wanted. . . ." "So the very arguments of the evolutionist recoil upon himself. We see that his appeal to embryology must be unsound in any case."

Ballantyne, an expert in embryology, writing in a standard text book says: "Ontogeny does not give a short recapitulation of evolutionary progress: it is not an epitomised Phylogeny" (Green's *Encyclopaedia and Dictionary of Medicine and Surgery*, vol. 3, p. 73). Again, Adam Sedgwick in his article "The Influence of Darwin on the Study of Animal Embryology" in *Darwin and Modern Science*, page 173, states: "In the first place it must be noted that the recapitulation theory is itself a deduction from the theory of evolution . . . the facts as we know them lend no support to the theory". T. H. Morgan calls the very appeal to embryology to prove evolutionary hypothesis "in principle false".

Another important point is this: If recapitulation is a fact there should be a parallel in the vegetable kingdom. But it has never been observed among plants. And Professor V. L. Kellog, himself an evolutionist, states in his book *Darwinism Today* (p. 15), "The recapitulation theory is mostly wrong, and what is right in it is so covered up by the wrong past that few biologists have any confidence in discovering the right". Experimental embryologists have no use for the theory. To Ehrlich and Hohn, Haeckel's biological law is only "biological mythology".

Such being the revealed facts one might well ask, How did the recapitulation theory obtain such a hold on scientists, when it was first formulated by Haeckel? The reason is not hard to discover, if we probe into its foundations. We shall also gain an insight into the way in which "scientific facts" are sometimes presented to the public by eminent men of science who support the theory of evolution. To avoid exaggeration, and to be fair to the evolutionists, we shall quote only Haeckel's own words of defence. When Dr. Brass accused him of deliberately falsifying the diagrams of other scientists, by adding a few vertebrae to the human embryo and taking away some from the monkey's, Haeckel's reply in the *Mauchner Allgemeine Zeitung* of January 1909 contained the following admission: "To put an end to the unsavoury dispute I begin at once with the contrite confession that a small number (6.3 per cent) of embryo diagrams are really forgeries in Dr. Brass's sense: These, namely, for which the observed material is so incomplete or insufficient as to compel us to fill in and reconstruct the missing links by hypothesis and comparative synthesis . . . I should feel utterly condemned and annihilated by the admission, were it not that hundreds of the best observers and most reputed biologists lie under the same charge. *The great majority of all morphological, anatomical, histological and embryological diagrams are not true to nature, but are more or less doctored, schematised, and reconstructed*". This quotation will give the reader some idea of the "facts" which form one basis for the theory of evolution.

Other instances of cleverly manoeuvering scientific facts to support the theory of evolution are not wanting. Many drawings and plaster of Paris reconstructions of missing links, etc., are nothing but "doctored and schematised" presentations. Some, like the Piltdown man, have been clearly exposed as fakes, while others still remain to be exposed. It is this which made Dr. W. R. Thompson, F.R.S., Director of the Commonwealth Institute of Biological Control, Ottawa, state in his introduction to *Everyman's Library Centennial Edition of Darwin's "Origin of Species"* (1963), that "the success of Darwinism was accompanied by a decline in scientific integrity".

CHAPTER 7

EVIDENCES
FROM BLOOD RELATIONSHIP

BLOOD PRECIPITATION TEST

This test is supposed to support the theory of evolution by demonstrating "blood relationship" that exists between man and the lower animals. George Nuttal of Cambridge, during his investigations which led to the discovery of vaccination, came across a by-product known as the anti-human serum. Human blood added to this liquid forms a thick white precipitate; with the blood of a bird there is no reaction, but the blood of mammals like lemurs, monkeys and chimpanzees yields varying degrees of precipitate, slightest in the case of lemurs and heaviest in that of chimpanzees. This similarity in the structure of the blood of man and ape is supposed to prove their common ancestry.

Now, it is true that some similarity exists between the blood of mammals, which may even admit of their being arranged in a graded system. But this chemical similarity cannot prove evolution. Pursuing the same logic we might conclude that the pen knife, the bread knife and the sword have evolved from a common iron ancestor! For there is a similarity in the chemical make-up of these articles, and they can be arranged in a graded system according to the degree of hardness of each. However, further research along the same lines has shown that the tiger and the whale are close of kin as are also the parrot and the ostrich. But such inconvenient facts are ignored by the evolutionist.

Blood analysis has revealed other interesting facts as shown by B. C. Nelson. The specific gravity of human blood is 1059; of the pig and hare 1060; of the frog 1055-1056; of the snake 1055, and the monkey's 1054-1059. From this table we can see that the frog and the snake are closer to man than the monkey, while our nearest relation is the pig!

It may look somewhat strange to base our relationship with the pig on flimsy evidence such as the similarity in the specific gravity of the blood. Yet the suggestion of a piggian ancestry was the theme for a University extension lecture in our country a few years ago by a learned professor of Zoology holding a Ph.D. degree of the University of London. Of course he had many other facts of similarity to support his thesis that we have closer ties with the pig than with the monkey or the ape!

But this is not all. If the blood test be a criterion of common ancestry, why not the milk test too? And chemical analysis shows that the animal which stands nearest to man, in this respect, is neither the monkey nor the pig but – the ass![1]

Some have even found support for this ancestry in the traditional customs of some primitive peoples. For among the tribal people in our country there is still the practice of feeding infants when they are born with ass's milk instead of human milk. To what ridiculous conclusions do evolutionists lead us at times!

PROOF FROM GEOGRAPHICAL DISTRIBUTION

The proof from blood precipitation test and the proof from geographical distribution have not been presented by evolutionists in recent years. However, they do find a place in some text books of zoology, and for that reason they are considered in this series.

The proof from geographical distribution essentially consists in setting up a ridiculous idea of special creation, not warranted by the Bible and knocking it down again by ridicule. And because such an idea of special creation is unthinkable, evolutionary interpretation for the present distribution of animals and plants presumably is correct. Charles Darwin noted the similarity between the fauna of the Galapagos Islands (500 miles off the west coast of South America) and those of the main continent, and argued that such similarity was inexplicable on the basis of special creation (i.e. the idea that each species was created separately in its particular locality). This interpretation of special creation is not implied in the Scriptures. For the Bible not only permits variation within the "kind" created but also clearly indicates that all land animals migrated from a single spot after the Genesis flood. Evolutionists argue that our finding marsupial mammals only in Australia is due to the fact that the continent got separated from other parts of the world before the other mammals evolved. To this Duperett's answer seems to be the right explanation. According to him the fauna of Australia and Tasmania is not an indigenous survival from the mesozoic era but come there by immigration at a recent epoch (*Transformations of Animal World*, p. 306). This agrees with the Scriptural account. However, on the question of distribution evolutionists themselves are sharply divided, and in the current debate this is not usually presented as evidence in favour of the theory of Evolution.

[1] For further discrepancies for protein structures contradicting popular views on evolution such as cytochrome C, insulin and other proteins see C.R.S. 1967, Vol. 4, No. 2, page 82.

CHAPTER 8

EXPERIMENTAL EVIDENCES

Of the various so-called evidences in favour of the theory of evolution published in the text books, the two most important are (1) the evidence from historical biology, or fossil evidence, and (2) the experimental evidence, or the evidence from the study of genetics. We have already seen the nature of evidence recorded on the rocks, under "Palaeontological Evidence". The next important evidence in favour of the theory of evolution, namely the experimental, may now be considered.

EXPERIMENTAL EVIDENCE

There are two main factors which bring about changes in organisms, namely environmental modifications and modifications brought about in the nuclear material of the germ cells. Of these the environmental influence is not of much consequence as it often dies with the individual without affecting its germ cells. As an example of variation produced by change of environment the case of the plant Dandelion (Taraxacum) can be cited. Cuttings from the same plant grown in lowland gardens under favourable conditions differ in many characteristics, including size, length of flowerstalk, shape of leaves, etc. from those grown in Alpine gardens under unfavourable conditions. The same phenomenon may be observed among animals like the molluscs, which show marked changes not only in the external morphology of the shell but also in the internal anatomy of the reproductive system through changes in the environment. Marked changes in size, build, etc., are also seen in embryos of the same litter developing in favourable and unfavourable positions within the uterus of a mother. However, such modifications brought about by mere changes in the environment, or by Lamarckian "use and disuse" of organs, etc., are of very little consequence in producing permanent changes of evolutionary significance.

On the other hand, changes produced in the germ cells are of greater consequence, as they are heritable and can bring about change in a group. We shall therefore confine ourselves to such heritable changes of modifying individuals and groups. It was Gregor Mendel, a contemporary of Darwin, who first began to study the nature of variation and to record the laws governing inheritance, by a series of experiments with the edible pea – Pisum Sativum. These laws were rediscovered in 1900 by Bateson and others, who experimented on various animals and plants, applying the same Mendelian principles. Their conclusion, along with those of T. H. Morgan, established the great science of Genetics – "a science seeking to trace the way in which the different manifestations of life are initiated and continued". With the discovery of micro-technique it was soon established that the seat of heritable variations among organisms is in the chromosomes of their germ cells. These chromosomes are specialised protoplasmic bodies which appear in the nucleus of living cells, especially at the time of division. The importance of chromosomes is due to the fact that they are vehicles of the ultra-microscopic genes which constitute the ultimate physical basis of the germ plasm, on which heredity depends.

It was further shown that the number and nature of the chromosomes for a particular species is always fixed, and any change in their number or nature produces a corresponding change in the organism. And it is now fairly well established that germinal variations are of two kinds:

(1) Gene mutations which are chemical changes taking place in the gene molecules and (2) Chromosomal changes which involve addition or deletion of whole or of parts of chromosomes, or changing the order of the genes in the chromosomes.

Soon T. H. Morgan and his colleagues were able to demonstrate the correspondence between changes produced in the chromosomes or in their genes, and their effect upon the fruitfly *Drosophila*. Further, Muller and his men were able to induce changes in the chromosomes or in their genes by artificial means such as chemicals, X-ray, etc., and to record their effect on the organism. For a time it looked as though the key to unlock the mystery of evolution was at hand, and during the last half century intense research was done both on plants and animals to produce new species by artificial means. However, the production of so-called new species was found to be only a demonstration of a phenomenon occurring in nature as polyploidy, wherein the number of chromosomes in the species is doubled or trebled, etc.

Many of our new garden plants are thus only *polyploids*. Here the increase in numbers of chromosomes is by whole multiples of the normal haploid numbers. Thus in chrysanthemum the diploid numbers of species run into 18, 36, 54, 72 and 90. "Species" formation through polyploidy occurs mostly as a result of hybridisation of two previously existing species (allopolyploidy) as in the classical example of crossing radish (Raphanus Salivus) and cabbage (Brassica oleracea) demonstrated by Karpechenko. On crossing *Raphanus Salivus* (radish) with *Brassica Oleracea* (cabbage) each with nine chromosomes, the F. 1 hybrid showed no pairing, 18 single chromosomes occurring at the reduction division. The unreduced egg and sperm of 18 chromosomes each, when fertilised, gave rise to seeds with 36 chromosomes — that is *double diploids or amphidiploids*. Of these 60 per cent were fertile and showed regular bivalent formation. But R. H. Richaria and H. W. Howard showed different results (see *Journal of Genetics*, vol. 139, pp. 1024, 1937) and unless Karpechenko's results are always obtainable it cannot be said that a stable new species among plants has been established.

No doubt today we know of many hybrids that breed true. Many of our flowering plants (about 35 per cent) are polyploids along with the crop plants like cotton, wheat, plums, sugar-cane, etc. But since no new characters are forthcoming in these polyploids, the range of variation that can be produced is limited. Thus even among plants, which are more plastic than animals, the range of variation seems to be strictly limited. Polyploids are also rare among animals.

MUTATIONS

Regarding changes among animals brought about by artificial mutations, most of the evidence is afforded by experiments on the fruitfly. More than 460 mutant forms of this insect "Drosophila" have been brought into being by the geneticists, but they are all fertile when crossed with the original species and can be made to revert back. These mutants are produced by alterations of the genes themselves, which may have a physical as well as a chemical make-up. Though the actual change in a gene cannot be exactly determined by the present technique, its effect in the mutant can be observed. Thus a red eye may become colourless, wings smaller or vestigial, and normal vision may be lost. It will be noticed that these changes are all degenerations.

Professor J. Muller, when he was awarded the Nobel Prize in 1946 for his work on mutations, summarised the results of his investigations in the following words: "Most of the mutations are bad. In fact the good ones are so rare that we can consider them all as bad" (Muller – *Time*, 11th November, 1946, p. 38). More recently Mayr (1963): "It can hardly be questioned that most visible mutations are deleterious." Since mutants are weaklings it is obvious that they have very little chance of survival, and can never become progenitors of a new species. Professor E. W. MacBride said, "Creatures with shrivelled-up wings and defective vision, or no eyes, offer poor material for evolutionary progress". Even if they can be reared under laboratory conditions the chances of their survival in the wild state are practically nil. It was this that made Professor Haldane state at a conference of the Biology Council held in Birmingham (December 1951), that Natural Selection weeds out extremes of all kinds, especially those caused by mutations which are very different from the normal. He said, "I regret to have to inform you that Natural Selection has not been observed to cause evolutionary change". During the same talk Professor Haldane gave it as his opinion that when two mutually sterile offspring had been bred from a common ancestor, as was done in the case of *Drosophila*, it could not be claimed that these were two new species. According to him, the geneticists have not yet succeeded in breeding a new species of *Drosophila*.

ACCUMULATION OF MUTATIONS

Even granting that advantageous mutations are occasionally produced, it will be another great problem to establish them in population. Though 26 generations of *Drosophila* can be observed in one year, and since 1910 to the present date more than a thousand generations have been observed (and even this rate of mutation can be speeded up by X-ray), so far *no* accumulation of mutations has been observed.

Dobzhansky and Tan are of the opinion that the slight differences between *Drosophila miranda* and *Drosophila pseudobscura* can be accounted for by the gradual accumulation of inversions and translocations. But at the same time Dobzhansky is conscious of the rarity of such translocation occurring in nature. In his *Genetics and Origin of Species*, page 115, he says, "The present writer has examined the salivary gland chromosomes in the offspring of between 10,000 and 20,000 individuals of *pseudobscura* taken from natural populations, without finding a single translocation. However, even if such translocations are found by chance, they are at a disadvantage in the struggle for existence. For no inversions or translocations have been shown experimentally to confer even one per cent selective advantage. Like mutations, they are very rare; and for them to become established in the population, even the geological times seem to be insufficient. Thus it is difficult to understand how the many kinds of mammals could have evolved in the comparatively short time since the beginning of the Tertiary period, even if we grant that the geologists are correct in their time estimates."

J. M. Coulter, in his *Science Remaking the World*, page 177, is of the opinion that "the new species formed by mutations are only species of the same physiological level, or declining in rank". According to him there is no adequate explanation of progressive evolution or the advance from one great phylum to another. Goldschmidt of the University of California reaches the same conclusion. In his *Material Basis of Evolution* he proves in detailed fashion that small mutations cannot add up to new species; and that the varieties so formed are not incipient species. In his book *Theoretical Genetics* he says, " . . . nobody has ever succeeded in producing a new species, not to mention the higher categories, by selection of micromutations". Again Rench (1959) says, "Most mutations cause a decrease in viability or fertility".

It is such results as these that made Professors Lysenko and Michurin of the U.S.S.R. bitterly oppose the work of Mendel and Morgan. According to Lysenko the researches of Morgan and others have only "led the biologists to a cul-de-sac", so far as evolutionary progress is concerned, and the varieties produced by them cannot represent incipient species. And Huxley said (1943): "It must be admitted that the direct and complete proof of the utilisation of mutations in evolution under natural conditions has not yet been given." As late as 1972, Dr. Nikolai Dubinin, member of the U.S.S.R. Academy of Sciences, said, "We no longer require genetic evolution. The new man will develop through social transformations". Contemporary social, scientific and technological revolution will bring staggering changes in man's intellectual world. Man's personality and abilities are not determined by genes.[1]

INHERITANCE OF ACQUIRED CHARACTERS

The Russian school is of the view that acquired characters are inherited and evolutionary change is due to external forces acting upon organisms. But this view has no confirmation outside Russia. On the other hand T. H. Morgan in his *Scientific Basis of Evolution* (1937), page 187, says, "It is not as generally known as it should be that the new work in genetics has struck a fatal blow at the old doctrine of the inheritance of acquired characters. The old doctrine held that modification of the body cells, produced during development or adult stages by means of external agencies, is inherited. In other words a change in the character of the body cells causes a corresponding change in the germ cells. A few examples will serve to show how genetics has undermined this already frail and mysterious doctrine. The custom of foot-binding, common for centuries among Chinese women, has not led to any inherited deformity of the foot; and our domestic fowl, a descendant of the Roman fowl, has not changed essentially in spite of two thousand generations of breeding."

Thus we have seen all that genetics can offer. There are four methods by which species are said to be changed, namely: (1) Natural Selection, (2) Transmission of acquired characters, (3) Hybridisation and (4) Mutation. Regarding natural selection we have already cited Professor Haldane's view, that "Natural selection has not been observed to cause evolutionary change". Our quotation from T. H. Morgan shows that acquired characters are not inherited. In regard to hybridisation and mutation, experiments already referred to have amply demonstrated the extraordinary stability of the species. Dr. Heribert Nilsson, Professor of Botany of the University of Lund, Sweden, has defined a species as "a sphere of variation". He states in his *Hereditas* (1953), page 252, that "variants are formed, out-crossed and arise anew, in a kaleidoscopic sequence within the species. But the species remains the same sphere of variation. The various species will remain like circles that do not intersect. *Species are constant.*"

MUTATIONS OSCILLATORY AND LESS VIABLE

Heribert Nilsson further states in his more recent book, *Synthetic Speciation* (published in German in 1954), "mutations are cyclic, they occur, reoccur after disappearing con-tinually in definite ratios". And since genes are large mole-cules, mutations according to him are "only expressions of the instability of the atomic chains". According to him, "mutations are not new, they have appeared many times in the history of the species but have disappeared again". Evolution by large variation is unlikely, as Morgan demon-strated as early as in 1925. He stressed in *The Genetics of Drosophila*, page 55, that "the further a character departs from the normal, the less viable it is". They are thus unfit to live and compete with others in the world. Small muta-tions, according to him, "only oscillate around the old one. . . . Furthermore, and this is fundamentally important, they will never be separated from the mother species because even the large mutations are fertile with it". An incompatibility which might cause a separation into different species is not found among the mutations whether they be super-great or sub-small. They intercross freely with the mother species. Regarding accumulation of mutations, Dr. Nilsson quotes the experiments of Gonzales (*American Nature*, vol. 57), showing that "the viability sinks on an average with the number of accumulated genes. A com-bination of five has a life-span only one quarter of that of the wild form, and its fertility does not even amount to one-fifth of that form."

The same experiments reveal that the physiological effect on a mutant gene (whether micro or macromutation), is to reduce its viability and fertility. Thus "mutations, even if they can surpass the mother species in certain respects, are nevertheless inferior in respect of total viability and therefore in competitive power".

In his great German publication *Synthetische Arbildung* (Synthetic Speciation) Dr. Heribert Nilsson has the following conclusions on page 177, "The innumerable mutations which indicate alterations in the genome (lowest haploid number of chromosomes), whether they be loss mutations, or gain mutations, macro or micromutations, viable or non-viable, as well as chromosome changes, all have this in common, that *they remain as oscillatory forms, or, at most, remarkable varieties within the species*, whereas if an evolutionary value is to be attached to them they must depart from the species population. According to modern genetical conceptions, this condition ought to be obvious, but although inevitable, it is unfortunately very little appreciated." Mutations therefore are mostly degenerations and whether gene mutations or chromosomal aberrations, they only lower the viability and competitive power of the species even if favourable mutations are accumulated. "According to Seigler[2] the so called 'evolution' is through the process of degeneration. All individuals of a plant or animal group must have originated through degeneration from the one created kind. The offspring species carry with them but a fraction of the hereditary variability found in the parent gene pool. Seigler contends that all these processes of change have been degenerative. Members of a single created kind can be distinguished by the fertility test even if the resulting embryo dies at an early stage of development.[3] And any change brought about by mutation may disappear as the mutants freely intercross with their parents. An incompatibility which might cause a separation into different species is not found among the mutations."

The only hope of geneticists in producing a variety of

any lasting value is in the phenomenon of *Polyploidy*. But this hardly exists among animals and so cannot account for the evolution of organisms in general. Polyploidy should be considered as a secondary phenomenon mainly observed among plants; polyploids have the same lowering of viability and consequent loss of competitive power as the mutants, and therefore are no promising material for progressive evolution. In Dr. Nilsson's words again: "The species is the supreme unit in nature, and not an artificial product of the taxonomist nor an evolutionary widening of a continuous stream of variations. As a sphere of variation the species is constant" (p. 1186).

ONLY BASIC KINDS WITH VARIATION IN NATURE

Experimental results accumulated for the last fifty years point to the conclusion that: "It is absolutely impossible to build a current evolution on mutations or on recombinations." Mayr (1963) "Through recombination a population can generate ample genotypic variability for many generations without any genetic input whatsoever". Only variations of the "basic kinds" which may even revert back to the original can be in nature at the present day. The two hundred and odd varieties of dogs, the varieties of sheep, oxen, horses, vegetables, wheat, etc. produced in this way are often offered as proof for evolution by the evolutionists. But it is a fact that not even a single new type of animal or plant has ever been produced. For no new genes arise by the introduction of new genetic material like D.N.A. Dobshansky (1953) observes, "The formation of new genes in evolution can be visualised only through radical modification of pre-existing ones". Dobshansky, in his *Genetics and the Origin of Species* (1941), page 3, admits the discontinuity that exists in nature among basic kinds: "If we assemble as many individuals living at a given time as we can, we notice at once that the observed variation does not form any kind of continuous distribution. Instead, a multitude of separate, discrete distributions are found. In other words the living world is not a single array of individuals in which any two variants are connected by unbroken series of intergrades, but an array of more or less distinctly separate arrays, intermediates between which are absent or at least rare." This is echoed by T. H. Morgan in his book, *Evolution and Adaptation*, on page 42, "Within the period of human history we do not know of a *single instance* of the transformation of one species into another one. . . . It may be claimed that the theory of descent is lacking, therefore, in the most essential feature that it needs to place the theory on a scientific basis. This must be admitted."

CONCLUSION

From the above accumulated facts it is clear that plants and animals are capable of variation within the basic kinds or species, but any attempt to go beyond this "sphere of variation" makes them more vulnerable and less fitted for survival. *Julian Huxley's proof of evolution* through mutation due to rearrangement in D.N.A. expressed in light and dark moths in England is disproved by Dr. H. B. D. Kettlewell in Scientific American showing that they are two colour phases of the same moths. It is only because of the smog in England that the trees have darkened. The camouflage that once protected the light moths is gone and the dark moths are now protected from the birds. There are no changes in the moths – but only the ratio of the population.[4] Thus the origin of no basic type of animal or plant can be demonstrated in the living world of today or in the rocky strata of the past. This indicates that evolution does not occur today and has not occurred in the past. Nevertheless some scientists are so obsessed with the idea of evolution that they are prepared to overlook these facts and assert by faith that one basic type can be changed into another basic type, provided sufficient time (millions of years) is available. But to the creationist the scientific facts discovered are in harmony with what is stated in the book of Genesis, namely the creation of certain basic types of organisms, each having the power to vary and adapt itself to its environment and reproducing only "after its kind" because "the seed is in itself". There is no contradiction between the Bible account of creation and the established facts of genetics and palaeontology.

[1] *The Madras Mail*, 21st September, 1972 on "New Theory of Evolution".
[2] Hilbert R. Seigler 1972 – *Evolution or Degeneration*.
[3] C.R.S. 1973, Vol. 10, No. 2, pages 125 and 126.
[4] *Scientific American*, Vol. 200, March, 1969.

Chapter 9

EVOLUTIONS AND

ORIGIN OF LIFE

Another important fact that challenges the evolutionist is his failure to offer any satisfactory explanation for the origin of life. The idea of Evolution has naturally been extended into the world of organic chemistry. Darwin himself speculated that spontaneous generation of life may have occurred by chance formation of proteid in "some warm little pond with all sorts of ammonia and phosphoric acid salts, light, heat and electricity". Since his day various attempts have been made by organic chemists and bio-chemists to produce life in the laboratory. All such attempts have proved failures. From the time of Louis Pasteur to this day research continues to demonstrate the fact that only life can produce life. All that has been achieved so far is only the formation of organic compounds from inorganic substances. Some simple amino acids like glycine were produced by activating by electric spark a mixture of simple inorganic substances like hydrogen, water vapour, methane and ammonia. It was hoped that, given time, life would arise in the sea from such spontaneously produced amino acids. But so far (1965) in spite of innumerable attempts, scientists have not succeeded in producing a single cell or even a single molecule like the D.N.A. molecule. Dr. Harzobind Khorona, the Indian Scientist who was awarded the Nobel prize for discovering genetic code in 1968, synthesised a total gene from simple organic substances.[1]

Our hope of producing life seems to be dwindling away as our knowledge of cell chemistry advances. There was a time when the single-celled animals were considered to be primitive forms of life. But detailed study of the working of living cells has revealed the amazing complexity of their mechanism. It is a well-known fact that even if such organic complex compounds are manufactured, the oxygen in the air or existing organisms would quickly kill them. Complex molecules need living material to protect them. They cannot exist independent of their living cells. According to J. J. Grebe, a physical chemist (1964), "the cell has been found to be so complex that the longest time that everybody wants to ascribe to the age of the Universe or the Earth, is just plain trivial compared to the time that it would take to make one living cell from exactly right raw materials under the most ideal conditions and with a frequency of, say, one per second, for assembly and test and evaluation by the survival of the fittest . . .". "Scientists could not even show the most trivial chance of producing one single D.N.A. molecule with 10^{87} varieties possible that would be able to match the R.N.A. at the same time by any kind of a process even conceding stable planes as proven substratas assumed to be available at all times. After all, 10^{17} seconds is all that the maximum age of the earth provides, and what is that against 10^{87}?" (quoted from *Creation Research Society Quarterly*, vol. 1, No. 1, July 1964, p. 5).

It is recently claimed that D.N.A. and R.N.A. can be produced in the laboratory. But this does not solve the problem of spontaneous generation of life or one kind evolving into another. According to B. Commoner's article in *Scientific Research*, October 1966, page 33, "D.N.A. is neither a self-sufficient genetic code, nor the master chemical of the cell". Further, self-duplication is a property of the whole intact cell and D.N.A. molecules by themselves do not in fact reproduce in test tubes. Thus one created kind becoming another kind becomes all the more difficult.[2]

Report in *The Madras Mail*, daily paper dated 18th May, 1973, states that Dr. Khorona completed a gene in 1970 and is completing another new gene. However, at present no one knows how to get a synthetic gene into a human cell, not to mention how to get the doctored cell to thrive and multiply in the human body.

In a 1964 article on spontaneous creation of life Dr. Zimmerman (chemist) said: "Modern bio-chemical research has served to unravel much of the mystery of the chemistry of life. But in the unravelling of the vast complex of cell chemistry it has exposed still more the statistical improbability so large as to be equated with 'impossible'. Like the mystery of the atom the mystery of life also evades scientific investigation. Life suddenly appeared on earth not as a tiny speck of protoplasm, as evolutionists tell us, but as the Bible tells us, as different kinds of animals and plants – capable of variation within limits, but always reproducing only 'after their kind'."

DID LIFE ARISE FROM PRIMITIVE FORMS LIKE THE VIRUS?

Viruses are the smallest of all living things, and in the evolutionist's language they are the most "primitive". Essentially they consist of a protein molecule containing protein and nucleic acid. They are so small that they can be seen only under the Electron Microscope. As the name suggests, viruses are mostly poisonous, causing diseases like small-pox, polio, yellow fever, etc. According to the Bible, disease and death are the consequences of man's sin.

Some years ago evolutionists imagined that viruses, being the smallest and simplest of organisms and capable of even crystallisation, could be produced in a test-tube. Various attempts were made in this direction. But all that could be done was to split the virus into its basic components – protein and nucleic acid – and recombine them again. As they are incapable of independent existence, like parasites they can only live inside host cells which are more complicated. It is therefore evident that viruses cannot be "primitive" organisms as was once believed by evolutionists. For they could have come into existence only after the creation of the more complicated host cells!

Viruses are also incapable of producing amino acids and are not able to synthesise their own structure from a mixture of amino acids. Amino acids in Nature are available either from the breakdown of other living matters or from the living plants which manufacture them. Viruses therefore can never be considered as having come into existence earlier than other plants and animals which manufacture amino acids. Genetically they behave as any other higher plant or animal. They all reproduce "after their kind". They do not arise "*de novo*". A mixture of amino acids, nucleic acids and proteins, etc., even under the most ideal conditions do not give rise to viruses. Viruses can no longer be considered as primitive forms of life. In fact there is nothing primitive in God's creation. Whether it be virus, bacteria or protozoa, they are all created in perfect beauty and are complete and finished products. Even the microscopic diatoms have their own beauty and complexity.

We therefore infer that Darwin's surmise that all the organisms which now exist or have existed have developed from a few extremely simple primitive form or forms is no longer tenable. For there is nothing so simple or primitive in God's creation.

[1] *The Madras Mail*, 3rd June, 1970.
[2] C.R.S. 1967, Vol. 4, No. 1, page 50.

CHAPTER 10

ORIGIN OF MATTER

"The theory of evolution is totally inadequate to explain the origin and manifestation of the inorganic world," said Sir Ambrose Fleming, F.R.S. (discoverer of the thermionic valve) in the early part of this century. The same challenge faces the evolutionist today regarding the origin of matter, in spite of the tremendous advances that science has made during the last fifty years. Regarding the origin of the universe various theories were put forward one after the other. Laplace's nebular hypothesis, which was favourably considered by the leading scientists of the 19th century, was subsequently abandoned. This theory held that the material forming the sun and the planets was in the form of a hot rotating gaseous mass, and that gases flung out from the equator of this rotating mass in the form of rings, split up and cooled, giving rise to the various planets of the Solar System. But this theory on mathematical calculations was found to be unworkable. Later Sir James Jeans put forward the theory of the wandering stars pinching away masses of gas which cooled and became planets. Subsequent to this, the collision theory, and several others, were proposed. But every one of them had to be abandoned as inadequate to explain the facts. Gamow and other cosmogonists have come back to the Nebular Hypothesis with certain modifications. According to George Gamow's "Big Bang Theory" the Universe started from a highly condensed core of protons and neutrons which exploded in a big bang about five billion years ago.

But none of these great men were able to explain the manner in which the original Nebula or material came into being. This gap in our knowledge will ever remain, as science does not and cannot deal with origins. Fred Hoyle, Professor of Astronomy at Cambridge, says in *Harper's Magazine*, February, 1951, as quoted by Zimmerman: "I find myself *forced to assume* that the nature of the universe requires continuous creation – the perpetual bringing into being of new background material. . . . The most obvious question to ask about continuous creation is this: Where does the created material come from? It does not come from anywhere. Material appeared . . . it is created. At one time the various atoms composing the material do not exist and at a later time they do. This may seem a very strange idea and I agree that it is, but in science it does not matter how strange an idea may seem, so long as it works. . . . Hydrogen is being steadily converted into helium throughout the universe, and this conversion is a one way process . . . that is to say, hydrogen cannot be produced in any appreciable quantity through the breakdown of other elements. How comes it then that the universe consists almost entirely of hydrogen? If matter were infinitely old, this would be quite impossible. So we see that the Universe being what it is, the creation issue cannot simply be dodged. And I think, of all the various possibilities that have been suggested, continuous creation is easily the most satisfactory."

Fred Hoyle is contradicted by his own colleague Professor Martyn Ryle (1961) of Cambridge University, who believes in a definite creation of the Universe, and that it will not continue forever. This is the Biblical view, and science agrees with it. Further, we know that the sun gives out energy in the form of heat and light at a rate which can be calculated. About 250 million tons of its mass is being annihilated per minute. The same process of annihilation must have been going on in the stars also. The whole universe is melting away into radiant energy. In Sir James Jeans' words, "The universe is like a clock which is running down, which, so far as science knows, no one ever winds up. It is at present a partially wound up clock, which must at some time in the past have been wound up in some manner unknown to us". He further states, "Everything points with overwhelming force to a definite creation or series of events of creation at some time or times not infinitely remote. The universe cannot have originated by chance out of the present ingredients, neither can it always have been the same now". Lord Kelvin said: "Science positively demands creation."

These scientific ideas are better expressed by the psalmist in Psalm 102: 25-27. "Of old hast thou laid the foundation of the earth: and the heavens are the work of thy hands. They shall perish but thou shalt endure: yea, all of them shall wax old like a garment; as a vesture shalt thou change them, and they shall be changed. But thou art the same, and thy years shall have no end." With all due respect, Professor Hoyle's theory of hydrogen coming out of nothing continuously is quite unscientific and merely begs the question.

The changes observed throughout the physical universe are caused by running down and not by building up. Complex atoms like uranium and thorium disintegrate into less complex ones like radium or lead, but never in the reverse order. How then, can evolution, a process of building up from simpler to more complex forms, take place in nature? It is contrary to a well established law of physics, namely, the Second Law of Thermodynamics. In an article on the origin of the Universe that appeared in *Creation Research Society's Quarterly*, vol. 1, No. 1, dated July 1964, Dr. Donald O. Acrey, Geophysicist, concludes as follows: "I visualise the creation of the universe as recorded in Genesis with light waves moving at the instant of the creation of the heavens and the earth. Such an idea should be readily acceptable, since the transformation of the proton (the raw power of the Universe) to an atom takes only minutes, and from atom to molecule additional minutes and thence to all matter a few hours. The accurate determination of the age of the Universe is dependent upon ascertaining the refraction, diffraction and diffusion characteristic of light through measured intervals of space. The proper tools and techniques are not to be found to do this." It may therefore be said that the deeper the probe made by science to unravel the secret of the origin of life or matter, the greater the mystery that is found to enshroud them. However, facts not theories, so far established in science have failed to contradict God's revelation written in the Bible.

CHAPTER 11

DISADVANTAGES
OF EVOLUTION

Evolutionists often contend that the doctrine as proposed by Charles Darwin has been a great stimulus to scientific thinking as a whole, and biological sciences in particular. The writer begs to differ from such a view. It is true that the theory of evolution acted as a stimulus to biological research for a time. But the nature of the stimulus was such that it has stimulated biologists to let in clouds of speculation into scientific research. Much time was wasted in determining the systematic position and relationship between the basic kinds of animals and plants. Many hypothetical ancestors were invented to bridge the gaps existing between the basic kinds, consequent on assumptions that they were descended from a common ancestor. Almost every invertebrate phylum was postulated as the ancestor of vertebrates. Much time was wasted in trying to fit the facts of embryology into the biogenetic "law" and prove the theory of evolution. Only after much study and unfruitful labour, Professor Westoll could call such embryological evidence for evolution "sheer nonsense". Likewise breeding experiments carried on for years, and on more than a thousand generations, only led Morgan and his school to the *"cul-de-sac"* of Lysenko. Such ceaseless attempts of evolutionists to fit scientific facts into the evolutionary mould have in fact delayed the progress of biological science. The same effect has also introduced much futile speculation into scientific thinking.

Since the knowledge of fossils was meagre, and experimental data in breeding experiments were inadequate, Charles Darwin had to support his theory by speculative arguments and assumptions. Throughout his book *Origin of Species* expressions such as "we may therefore assume", "it is possible", "it may be supposed", etc., are often used instead of definite statements of facts. As Professor W. R. Thompson has put it: "Personal convictions and simple possibilities are presented as if they were proofs, or at least valid arguments in favour of the theory." Darwin could not prove the origin of any species. All that he did was to present certain observed facts of nature and by persuasive arguments show how species might have originated. But these assumptions of Darwin were not true to the facts that have come to light since his day. However, he left a legacy for biological sciences which cannot easily be disinherited, namely, that of speculative thinking. In this art some of his followers have excelled him.

A classic example of such imaginative speculation is cited by Professor W. R. Thompson in his introduction to the latest edition of *Origin of Species* (1963), page 21: "In the article on 'Mimicry' in the 14th edition of the *Encyclopedia Britannica*, we find a remarkable explanation of the form of a tropical insect belonging to the group of 'lantern flies'. The head of this insect, which is not very large, resembles in miniature the head of an alligator, being prolonged into a snout at the base of which is a protuberance resembling an eye, while along the side are formations resembling minute teeth. Curious though the resemblance is, it is obviously a coincidence. The insect as a whole does not look anything like an alligator. However for the Darwinian author of the article we have here an example of the development of protective resemblance by natural selection. The similarity of the head of an insect to the head of an alligator is a protection against monkeys. The monkey does not actually mistake the insect for an alligator, but the sight of its head recalls to him the occasion in which an alligator almost

seized him when he was drinking from a stream. Such is the effect of Darwinian fantasy on biological thinking." Some biologists are so obsessed with the idea of evolution, that scientific facts which do not fit into the evolutionary pattern are rejected or suppressed or sometimes even "*deliberately falsified*".

Thus under the blood test, we have already seen how facts showing a closer blood relationship between the tiger and the whale were rejected, and only those facts which served to support the evolutionist's doctrine were made known. Even such a man of great scientific reputation as Sir Arthur Keith is accused of having deliberately suppressed the facts about the skulls of men found at Calavaras and Castenedolo, which were older than all the "apemen" ever discovered. In an article on Evolution in the *Encyclopedia Britannica* he mentioned only "Pithecanthropus" instead of the "Castnedolo" finds. The same may be said of Professor E. Dubois who suppressed the find of true human remains (the Wadjak skulls) found at Java on the same strata as Pithecanthropus (Java ape-man). Why such suppression of facts? Because they did not fit into the evolutionary pattern. If only these scientists had mentioned the facts about these earlier truly human finds, much, if not all, of the speculations regarding ape-human ancestry could have been avoided. Cases of deliberately falsifying or faking evidences in order to support the theory of evolution are not wanting elsewhere. Haeckel's confession of falsifying diagrams of embryos to establish his biogenetic law has already been pointed out. Suffice it to say that his statement "that hundreds of the best observers, and most reputed biologists lie under the same charge", cannot be lightly dismissed.

Another instance of a deliberate hoax is seen in the manner in which Dawson and his friends concocted the Piltdown man. This has been exposed by evolutionists themselves, though forty years later. This is what made Professor W. R. Thompson state that "the success of

Darwinism was accompanied by a decline in scientific integrity". The advent of the theory of evolution, therefore, has not only delayed the progress of biological sciences, but has also encouraged speculation and falsification of scientific facts.

The time has come for evolutionists to regain the confidence of the public which they lost by adopting such tactics. This can only be achieved when scientists are free from their obsession with the philosophy of evolution and set themselves to seek truth for its own sake. Only then, can creationists and evolutionists work side by side in discovering the laws underlying the whole creation. Then creationists and evolutionists will agree with each other in so far as the facts of science are concerned. But where science ends and philosophy begins, they are bound to differ. Scientists who choose to follow the philosophy of creation may continue to believe in the Biblical record of creation; and scientists who prefer to believe in the philosophy of evolution may choose to follow evolution. But the superiority of the creationist's philosophy will be that added satisfaction of finding a harmony between the facts of science and the statements of the Bible. He will also find that his moral and spiritual faculties are satisfied, which the evolutionists ignore.

CHAPTER 12

SPECIAL CREATION

The only alternative to evolution is special creation. Even Sir Arthur Keith, who wrote the introduction to *Origin of Species* more than a quarter of a century ago said: "Evolution is unproved and unprovable. We believe it because *the only alternative is special creation which is unthinkable*." The first part of Keith's statement has been fully verified and we are forced to conclude with Louis Agassiz that "the theory is a scientific mistake". We therefore wish to re-examine the facts of science now known to us with a view to investigate whether the theory of special creation is unthinkable or not.

There is no need to define special creation as it is clearly recorded in the first chapter of the book of Genesis in the Bible. According to special creation, God created the heavens and the earth in six days by His divine power, bringing into being the different "kinds" of animals and plants, with power to reproduce "after their kind" and replenish the earth. It is the writer's contention that this account of creation is in no way contradicted by the established facts of science as we know them today. However it must be admitted that this account of creation has been understood differently by different people. For instance Linne (1707-1778): the use of the word "species" in his classification is not identical with the "kind" mentioned in the Bible. Many Linnaean species like Equus Caballus (Horse), Equus asinus (Ass) and Equus Zebra (Zebra) may all be thought of as the "horse kind" just as the lion, tiger, etc., can be included in the "felis" or "cat" kind. Hybrids between these "species" can artificially be produced but hybrids between the basic kinds created by God can never be produced. For instance, a hybrid between a cat and dog or a hybrid between a man and an ape is never produced. The "kind" of the Bible, then, is a much broader group than the "species" of the taxonomist as generally understood.

Even among evolutionists the term "species" is a widely disputed term. As Dr. Marsh in his book *Evolution, Creation and Science* points out, one of the most modern ideas of evolutionists is, "that it is frequently a polytypic group composed of several to many geographical races". This understanding of the term "species" brings the evolutionist nearer the creationist's "kind". True Biblical "kinds" seem to be "physiologically isolated groups" each almost made of different materials. And this is why one basic kind does not give rise to another basic kind, no matter how many millions of years are allowed. In this sense the gap between the "created kinds" remains true from the beginning of creation.

Louis Agassiz's (1807-1873) view of special creation also differs from the modern concept. He believed that the blind fish in the mammoth cave was created and placed there by the Creator. This kind of fixity of species is not stated in the Genesis record. For the Bible speaks of mankind having originated from a single pair, and yet recognises the difference between a Jew and an Ethiopian; between normal men and giants. It only speaks of kinds reproducing "after their kind" because "the seed is in itself". Variations occur but they are strictly limited "within the kind". And this fact is now fully supported by both Palaeontology and Genetics. Modern biological science, therefore, only confirms the Genesis record.

Evolutionists used to believe that variation was unlimited and progressive, but modern facts of biology no longer support this assumption. Variation is now found to be occurring only within the "isolated physiological groups" or "kinds" created by God. For example all the varieties of dogs have come out of a single wild species of dog. The same may be said of the number of varieties of sweet peas, or the various races of men. If the occurrence of such variations within limits is termed evolution, then the special creationist is an evolutionist, and the evolutionist also, is a special creationist. In a talk given by Professor Julian Huxley on Evolution (in the College where the writer happened to be a Professor) the learned lecturer explained with slides how moths became spotted during the industrial revolution, citing that as a proof of evolution. Recently (January 1965) Professor Waddington spoke in Madras of the small changes brought about in the antenna of the fruitfly, Drosophila, due to environmental changes, as a "proof" of evolution. His talk was on the *New Theory of Evolution*. His thesis was that acquired characters were genetically absorbed, somehow, and passed on to the progeny through Natural Selection. Special creationists can agree with these minor changes brought about in animals and plants through environmental changes, if they are established facts of Science. But this is no proof of evolution as conceived by Charles Darwin. The special creationist is aware of greater changes that have come upon the single "kind" of homo sapiens, changes not only in colour but also in features and size. But this is not evolution. This is only variation within the created kind as recorded in the Bible. See Mayr (1963), "Mutations merely increase the heterozygosity of population but do not lead to the production of new species".

This doctrine of creation differs from the idea of fixity of species held by some in the past. It fully recognises the variations produced by all the genetical processes according to Mendelian principles, both among plants and animals, including mankind. At the same time it is aware of the limitations imposed on the range of variations, which is always within the "kind" created. It does not teach that man descended from any of the beasts directly or indirectly. But that he was created a perfect being, subsequently degraded by sin and the curse. It recognises the destruction of all land animals (including man) through Noah's flood, and the survival and repopulation of the world by those saved in the Ark. It recognises the moral and spiritual faculties of man and therefore does not lead man away from his Creator. On the contrary, this doctrine of creation restores him to his Creator by demonstrating the harmony between the facts of nature and God's revelation in the Bible.

EVIDENCES IN FAVOUR OF CREATION: DESIGN

The Bible says, "In the beginning God created the heavens and the earth". Witness to God and His creation is not wanting in the cosmic world. Both to a casual observer and to the student of details, the universe speaks of a design. In Einstein's words, "The scientist's religious feeling takes the form of a rapturous amazement at the harmony of natural law, which reveals an intelligence of such superiority that, compared with it, all the systematic thinking and acting of human beings is an utterly insignificant reflection" (*The World As I See It*, p. 9). For instance, the size of the universe as revealed by the 200-inch telescope reaching out to a distance of two billion light years, with its billions of stars and their planets, all moving in their own orbits with such clock-like precision, without any confusion, speaks of an all-wise and Almighty Creator who not only created them, but also keeps them going. The amazing accuracy with which the earth revolves round the sun year after year, taking exactly 365 days, 5 hours, 48 minutes and 48 seconds like a flawless machine, speaks of the master Engineer, and His perfect design. Who could have started the planets in motion, each on its own orbit and regularly proportioned in their distances from the Sun? Who is keeping them moving continuously? Such marvellous accuracy and precision cannot come into being through fortuitous chance operations, as evolutionists contend. None of the theories put forward by the cosmologists, be it Laplace's "Nebular Hypothesis" or Fred Hoyle's "Steady State Theory" or Gamow's "Big Bang Theory" can adequately account for such marvellous design. In Psalm 33: 6, 9 it is said, "By the word of the Lord were the heavens made, and all the hosts of them by the breath of his mouth. For he spake and it was done. He commanded and it sood fast."

The earth, designed for our habitation, is "weighed" and hung upon nothing (Job 26: 7). Her mass and size is adjusted to retain atmosphere and water in exactly the right proportion to maintain life. She is kept at the right distance from the sun, to be neither too cold nor too hot. She is tilted, unlike the other planets, at an angle of $23°$, to give seasons of the year for sowing and reaping the harvest. Lest the earth be washed by the waves of the sea, the moon is kept at the right distance from her. Who calculated and placed the moon? What about the atmosphere of the earth? It is weighed and kept balanced, that the lighter nitrogen may go up and the heavier oxygen may come down every time we breathe. What about the mystery of the formation of ice at $4°C$? and the wonderful design and beauty of snow flakes? What of the mystery now revealed inside the atom? Who could have reversed the law of electricity within the atom, that positive charges should attract positive charges among the protons? The Bible says, "the heavens declare the glory of God and the firmament showeth his handiwork".

The same handiwork of the Creator is also revealed among animals and plants. The marvellous way in which the eye of man is constructed is clear evidence of God's handiwork. The following may be quoted from Dr. Tyndall's *Through Science to God:* "Beneath the retina is a bacillary layer known as Jacob's membrance; this consists of 8 to 10 millions of rods and cones of varying lengths and vibratory rates. Each rod and cone is in tune with its own particular vibration in the light waves, and with no other.

Light falls on the retina and comes into contact with the rods and cones whose vibratory rate is in unison with the vibrations in the light waves; all the others remain quiescent. . . ."

"Those vibrations which are between 13 and 35,000 per second, the ear detects and we term them sound. Thirty-three octaves above the range of hearing, are electro-magnetic vibrations which we designate 'light'. There is one octave of these, or a trifle less. When 434 trillion vibrations a second fall upon rods and cones whose vibratory note is in unison with that number, we experience the sensation known as the colour 'red'; 500 trillion such vibrations are known as 'orange'; 520 trillion vibrations as 'yellow'; 570 trillion vibrations 'green'; 634 trillion 'blue'; 690 trillion 'indigo' and 740 trillion 'violet.' "

It would take volumes to describe the marvels of design in the bee and her hive, in the spider and his web, and thousands of such adaptation designs in nature. These could not have been developed by the accumulation of mere hit-and-miss chance variations. Dr. Charles Tyndall says, "He who looks deeply into nature's secrets should be the last to lose sight of her unity and uniformity and, hence, the unity and intelligence of the Author".

INSTINCTS

Again looking at instincts, we find that every animal is not only equipped with its own structure and form but is also provided with an instinct suitable to its own mode of life. Thus each bird builds its own peculiar nest according to the instinct given to it. There is no evolution or even improvement of nests seen among them with the passage of time. The apes which built their crude nests of leaves have not improved their lot and taken to mud houses, although men endowed "with wisdom from on high" have moved from mud huts into airconditioned rooms. Without any training or memories of the past, every generation of birds is capable of migrating thousands of miles over unknown lands and seas to the very spot of the earth where their parents once roosted. They do so by the instinct with which they are created. Likewise, every generation of wasps knows how to sting the caterpillar at the exact spot of its nervous system just to keep it paralysed, but alive, as prey for their developing young. More wonderful still is the instinct of that small silvery fish the grunion. The timely spawning of their eggs, the fertilisation by the males, and the gathering of the fry, are marvels of God's handiwork. The pregnant female grunions lay their eggs in the sand on Californian beaches exactly 15 minutes after high tide the night after the fortnightly high tide. These eggs have to be fertilised by the males within 30 seconds. Then these fertilised eggs buried in the sand are safe till the next high tide, a fortnight later. By that time the eggs develop; with the next high tide they hatch out suddenly when touched by salt water, and the new born fry are washed back into the sea by the receding waves. The question is, who taught grunions to time the tides? And who fixed the incubation period of the eggs to synchronise with the next high tide? And who adjusted the pull of the sun and the moon to be timed with the spawning of grunions? It is a clear demonstration of the marvellous design and the handiwork of an all-wise Creator. It is He who endowed the grunions with the right instinct to discern the time and tide.

LAW AND ORDER

Law and order are by no means confined to the heavenly bodies. They are apparent also in the tiny atom, which is now known to be a "universe within a universe". We see one law applicable to all matter outside the atom – the law of positive repelling positive charges – and quite another law governing the protons (charges within the nucleus of an atom). Inside the atom positive charges attract each other. This is a mystery. How came out the reversal of a "law" of nature? Science has no explanation for this "mystery of the universe" within the atom. But the Bible says (referring to

the Lord Jesus Christ): "By him were all things created that
are in heaven and that are in earth, visible and invisible . . .
and he is before all things, and by him all things consist (or
hold together)." Thus the study of physics leads us to
innumerable laws governing matter and energy. And
chemistry teaches us that the elements in nature do not
chemically combine with each other as they like, but
according to the laws already determined. If two atoms of
hydrogen gas combine with one atom of oxygen gas they
will always and invariably produce water, a liquid. This is a
fixed law of nature, which no man can alter. And there can
be no law without a Lawgiver.

BALANCE IN NATURE

The universal interdependence of all life on Earth is another
clear witness of a "Master mind" behind the creation. All
life forms a wonderful unit. As one author put it, "Nature's
world is peopled by no random assemblage of isolated,
unrelated forms of life jumbled together without rhyme or
reason. Rather, it is an inconceivably vast and integrated
organisation". There is a perfect balance maintained in
nature, not only among animals but also between animals
and plants, and even between the living and the non-living.
Checks and counter-checks are everywhere in nature to
maintain the balance, lest promiscuity should overrun the
earth. For instance, flying insects which can multiply
rapidly are kept in check by the bats and birds. Large fishes
eat the more prolific smaller fish, and the smaller mammals
are preyed upon by their larger predators. Evolutionists
contend that insects evolved long before the birds, their
predators, came in. If that were so, insects would have
destroyed all the available vegetation, and higher life could
not have evolved. The Bible informs us that all life was
created in six days. Only thus could the balance in nature
have been maintained.

Charles Darwin's example of the effect of cats on red
clover is a good illustration of the inter-dependence of

plants and animals. He says, "If field mice are not kept in check by cats, the nests of bumble bees would be destroyed by too many mice; with no bumble bees the red clover could not be fertilised, and would soon die out". What a beautiful instance of interdependence! Further, the bumble bee's size, weight, and mouth parts, etc. are so well adapted to effect pollination in red clover, that no other insect can do this job. Here we see that the flower and the bee are designed for each other by the great Designer.

The interdependence of the Yucca plant of the desert and the Pronuba moth is another wonderful example. Such a complicated and perfectly balanced relationship could never have "happened" by the fortuitous variations and adjustments of evolution. It can be explained only by terms of an all-wise Designer and Creator.

ORIGIN OF LIFE

Then again, for the spontaneous generation of life evolutionists believe that mere interaction of chemical constituents of protoplasm as such is not adequate, but that certain very special and improbable conditions of atmosphere are indispensable. They assume such ideal conditions to have existed at the beginning, and hope that they can be repeated. But biochemical investigations so far conducted indicate that this task is not so simple. In an article on spontaneous generation of life published in the Annual of the *Creation Research Scientists' Society* (1964) Dr. Paul A. Zimmerman of Michigan, writes as follows: "Most scientists agree that the original environment must have been free of oxygen. Oxygen in the atmosphere would effectively oxidise any early organic molecules and prevent the development of life. It would also, by the formation of ozone, effectively shield the earth's surface from the high-energy ultraviolet radiation required by the theories. On the other hand, ultraviolet light has a lethal effect on living organisms. If it were not filtered out by the atmosphere, no life could exist today. It thus seems a most unlikely source upon which to depend for starting life." He concluded the article in the following words: "Modern biochemical research has served to reveal much of the mystery of the chemistry of life. But in the unravelling of the vast complex of cell chemistry, it has exposed still more the statistical improbability of spontaneous generation. It is an improbability so large as to be equated with impossibility." These facts illustrate how life is dependent upon so many synchronising factors, which are essential not only for the maintenance of life but also for its origin. There are millions of protein molecules even in a single cell. These molecules and other particles in the cell would also need to be focused at the same place and at the same time. The odds against such happening accidentally would be a number that the world cannot contain. But then, you would still have dead protein in a dead cell. Recently Dr. I. J. Frankby the famed physicist, who was lecturing on nucleo synthesis in stellar processes, surprised his audience by claiming that he believed in special creation. He said, "The fact that *true science refutes* the theory that living matter and life have evolved from dead inanimate matter, leaves us with only one acceptable alternative. This alternative is Special Creation of God".

Even A. I. Oparin (1965) the Russian Biologist who fathered the theory of spontaneous generation wrote: "To the student of protein structure the spontaneous formation of such an atomic arrangement in the protein molecule would seem as improbable as would the accidental origin of the text of Virgil's *Aneid* from scattered letter type."[1] Only an all-knowing all-powerful Creator would have been able to produce matter out of nothing, and condition all the factors necessary for life on this planet at one and the same time.

Thus, whether we investigate the origin of life or of matter, or the splendour of this beautiful and orderly universe – from the tiny atom to the distant galaxy of stars – in all these we see only the glory and majesty of an all-wise Creator. We may therefore agree with Dr. Einstein that "the scientist's religious feeling takes the form of rapturous amazement at the harmony of natural law, which reveals an intelligence of such superiority that, compared with it, all the systematic thinking and acting of human beings is an utterly insignificant reflection".[2]

1 *The Origin of Life*. Second edition, page 133.
2 *The world as I see it*, page 9.

CHAPTER 13

EVOLUTION AND MAN

In 1856 a skeleton was dug out of clay in the Neander valley, near Dusseldorf. The skull was fairly squat and had pronounced brow ridges. The followers of Darwin acclaimed this find as a "link" between man and ape, and in 1856 it was classified as *Homo* (man) *Neanderthalensis*. Similar skeletons have since been unearthed in other parts of Europe. Then in 1890 a Dutch Doctor, Eugene Dubois, discovered in Java a primitive skull-cap, jaw-bone, and thigh bone, and named the new-found species *Pithecanthropus erectus* – "erect ape-man". Once again in the popular science magazines appeared pictures of a slouching hairy brute, alleged to be our "ancestor". In 1927 Franz Weidenreich discovered in a cave near Peking pieces of fifteen skulls and other bones. This species was named *Sinanthropus Pekinensis*. Like Pithecanthropus he was a full-sized "man" with a half-sized brain. Other finds have been Rhodesian "man" and Solo (Java) "man", both of which have gorilla-like faces but a brain as large as modern man's (homo sapiens). From 1924 onwards fossilised ape-men have been dug up in South Africa: they are collectively described as *Australopithecines*, which simply means "ape-like creatures of the south". More recently (1959) Dr. Leakey found in the Gorge of Olduva in Tanganyika a skull and crude tools of a human-like creature dating back (on his estimation) about 600,000 years. Dr. Leakey believes that this is the connecting link between ape-men and true men.

However, a very different view is expressed by the expert on anthropology who writes in a well-known British Encyclopaedia: "Up till fairly recently it had been held that homo sapiens had not been very long upon the earth and was a later development of the types of ape-man and half-brained men we have just been discussing. But it now seems probable that we must push back in time the origin of modern man to the very outset of the Middle Pleistocene. Also it is not now believed that Neanderthal man and his predecessors (except possibly Peking man) were in the direct line of descent of modern man. *In fact, his line of descent is completely unknown*, although we must assume that such a link exists." (That is, of course, *if* we assume that evolution is true.) Again: "These ape-men . . . were not ancestors of modern man, since, as is now generally believed, homo sapiens was in existence already at that time – the beginning of the Pleistocene – in other areas of Africa." Again: "In the first period, which started at the beginning of the Ice Age 700,000 years ago, homo sapiens was only one of a number of other types. . . . By the time the period was over (and this took 650,000 years) homo sapiens was monarch of all he surveyed and had eliminated his ape-like and half-brained rivals." (The "Ice Age" is the modern geologist's substitute for the Biblical Flood, which they deny ever took place.)

The reason why the ape-man, etc., cannot be our ancestors is that genuinely human remains have been found at geological levels equal or lower. The oldest skulls of man known to science are those found at Calavaras in North America and the perfectly human finds in Castenedolo, Italy. Sir Arthur Keith, in *The Antiquity of Man*, agreed that they are "genuine finds". About the skeletons of a man and two children he goes on to say: "As the student of pre-historic man reads and studies the records of the Castenedolo finds, a feeling of incredulity rises within him. He cannot reject the discovery as false without doing injury to his sense of truth, and he cannot accept it as a fact without

shattering his accepted beliefs (i.e. his belief in the evolution
of man). It is clear that we cannot pass Castenedolo by in
silence: all the problems relating to the origin and antiquity
of modern man focus themselves round it." Then let us
hear how Dr. W. H. Holmes, who investigated the Calavaras skull, presented his results to the Smithsonian Institute
in 1899: "To suppose that man could have remained
unchanged physically, mentally, socially, industrially and
aesthetically for a million of years, roughly speaking (and
all this is implied by the evidence furnished), seems in the
present state of our knowledge hardly less than a miracle!
It is equally difficult to believe that so many men should
have been mistaken as to what they saw and found."
Professor J. J. Duyvene De Wit says: "It has recently been
admitted by Robinson (1962), Mason (1962) and Leakey
(1961) that the *Australanthropines* can no longer be viewed
as the oldest relatives of *homo sapiens* because more human,
that is to say, less devoluted and brutalised forms have been
discovered who lived simultaneously with them and even
much earlier.

"Robinson expressed the opinion that *Telanthropus*
represents the superior race which, after invading the sites
where the inferior South African ape-like men lived, led to
their extinction by a more intelligent manufacture and use
of weapons. Very interesting is the discovery of Leakey in
one of the lower beds of Olduva Gorge (Tanganyika) of a
human *Pre-Zinjanthropus* form which probably lived half a
million years earlier than both the Australanthropines and
Zinjanthropus, and whose cranial bones and thus brain
volume were even larger than those of *Telanthropus*, thus
giving this form a more human appearance.

"Still more surprising is the discovery in a still lower
deposit of Olduva Gorge of an entirely new race of 'species'
of dwarfed men by Leakey and others (A.D. 1964). These
men to which the name *homo habilis* was assigned are
supposed to have lived almost two million years ago, and
in their morphology they appear surprisingly more *sapiens-*

like than the earlier mentioned younger regressive human forms.

"These discoveries prove, beyond any doubt, that in contrast to the transformist expectation of a straight-forward progressive evolution from a supposed ape-like ancestor to *homo sapiens*, the human species has given rise to a number of lines which clearly show distinct grades of *secondary retrogression* in the sense of *Le Gros Clark* (1962) and *Piveteau* (1962) while fossil remains of the genuine non-devoluted basic human stem have not been discovered so far.

"In the light of these recent discoveries it is not surprising that, in spite of being an adherer of the transformist doctrine, Leakey, as a scientist, recently claimed that his findings will revolutionise man's knowledge of his origin and will require the rewriting of anthropological text books in-cluding his own." (Quotation taken from *A New Critique of the Transformist Principle in Evolutionary Biology*, p. 57, by Professor J. J. Duyvene De Wit of Orange University.)

This is the dilemma with which the evolutionist is faced. Recently (1972) Richard Leaky, son of L. S. B. Leaky and Director of National Museum of Kenya discovered a human skull, thigh bone etc. from Rudolf Lake which has completely shattered the 50 year old theory of human evolution from Australopithicus. This specimen estimated to be 2.6 million years old is called "Adam" for his upright gait, brain capacity and normal skull bones. This finding of "Adam" has not only blasted all the previous speculations of human evolution from the ape or ape-like ancestors, but also now compels us to conclude that man was a separate creation from the beginning, being older than all the missing links and apes cited by evolutionists.

It appears that *homo sapiens* is older than all the "missing links"; but how could man with an intellectual capacity as large as our own have failed to discover and apply the arts and crafts of civilisation in a period two hundred times as long as that which separates us from Moses? The obvious answer is that the evolutionary time scale (as we have previously noticed) is hopelessly at fault, being based upon the unproved and unprovable assumption of *Uniformitarianism* in geology. If, on the other hand, we accept the Bible history as it stands, all (or *nearly* all) is explained. (1) Man was created perfect, in the image of God, about 6,000 years ago. Like the atom, he came from the hand of God a "finished product". Physically, morally, intellectually, and spiritually he was on a higher plane than ourselves. (2) Man fell into sin, and all his powers of body, mind and spirit, were corrupted. Neanderthal men, etc., if they had any connection with our race, may have been degenerate specimens which devolved from Adam in the centuries between the Creation and the Flood. Or they and the other "hominids" were species which God did not see fit to preserve when He sent the Flood, just as He did not see fit to preserve the dinosaurs. (3) Man did not have to "eliminate his rivals" because at the Flood all the hominids were destroyed together, and only their fossils remain. This would seem to fit in with the fact that many other sub-types of animal, such as *Eohippus*, were swept away never to re-appear. God washed the old world clean, and only allowed to survive as many species as would be necessary to populate the much harsher and less luxuriant world after the Deluge. At the same time *some* real men were buried alive and fossilised; but most would have climbed the hills attempting to escape the rising waters, and their drowned corpses would naturally have decomposed.

ARCHAEOLOGY AND POPULATION

Is there any other evidence of the antiquity, or modernity, of Man? Yes, there are two independent lines of study. Dr. Arnold J. Toynbee, one of the best-known historical scholars of our day, in the *Atlantic Monthly*, June 1942, wrote as follows: "As a matter of fact, 4004 B.C. happens to be quite an important date, though our ancestors did not know this: it marks approximately the first appearance of representa-

tives of the species of human society called civilisation. . . .
The first appearance of this species was about 6,000 years
ago." It is a fact that no records of any ancient civilisation
go back beyond 3000 B.C., which is the figure for Egypt and
Babylonia; and the age of pottery, monuments, etc., is
notoriously difficult to ascertain precisely. Ralph Linton, in
The Tree of Culture (1955), says: "The earliest Chinese date
which can be assigned with any probability is 2250 B.C.,
based on an astronomical reference in the *Book of History*."

Noteworthy also is the fact that the civilisations spring
into view *suddenly*. "The Great Pyramid of Khufu is
constructed of more than two million enormous blocks of
limestone each weighing two and a half tons in a structure
nearly 500 feet high and 570 feet square at the base. The
burial chamber lies at the bottom of a shaft beneath the
structure, and as in other pyramids there are additional
passages and chambers. Completed about 2885 B.C. by
300,000 men working for twenty years (St. Paul's, London,
took 35 years to build), this was the largest structure ever
erected by man, and even today it is only exceeded by the
Grand Coulee Dam in the United States. Yet only a century
before the Great Pyramid was built no stone building existed
anywhere in the world." Does this look like Evolution?

Incidentally the uncertainty which surrounds much
archaeological dating is well illustrated by the history of
the same Pyramid. In the 14th edition of *Encyclopaedia
Britannica* (1929), Professor Flinders Petrie, the leading
Egyptologist of his day, gives the date as 4700 B.C. Ten years
later the text books showed 3800 B.C., and now (1960) we
are told that 2885 B.C. will do!

The other line of argument is drawn from population
statistics. How long does it take for the human race to
double its numbers? Statisticians agree that about 150 years
is a reasonable average to assume, when allowance has been
made for wars, famines, etc. But the Bible gives us a more
accurate method of determining the doubling rate. According to an expert chronologist (E. R. Thiele in *The Mysterious*

Numbers of the Hebrew Kings, 1951) the marriage of Jacob,
father of the Jewish race, took place in 1930 B.C.; and before
Hitler's massacres (which must be judged exceptional)
world Jewry numbered nearly 16 million. This figure is
roughly 2^{24}; that is, it shows that the Jewish population has
doubled 24 times since the beginning. To determine the
rate of doubling, then, we have the following sum:

$$1930 \text{ B.C.}$$
$$+\ 1930 \text{ A.D. (Before Hitler)}$$

Total years since   ———
Jacob's marriage = 3860 years

Divide this figure by 24 and we get the doubling rate for
the Jewish race as *once every 161 years.*

Now according to the Bible genealogies the Flood took
place 589 years before Jacob's marriage, so the date will be:

$$\begin{array}{r} 1930 \\ +\ 589 \\ \hline = 2519 \text{ B.C.} \\ +\ 1965 \\ \hline \end{array}$$

Total years since the Flood   4484 years

The present population of the earth is approximately
2,500 million which is something over 2^{31}. And the population of the earth 4,484 years ago (according to the Bible)
was 8 or 2^3 (Noah and his wife, plus three sons and their
wives). So to find the doubling rate we must divide
4,484 by 28 (31-3). The answer is 160: so the doubling
rate of the entire human race has been *once every 160 years.*
Surely this is a very remarkable coincidence – or rather it
cannot be a "coincidence"! It is very strong evidence that
the Bible chronology is correct; and it shows that if the
Jewish race can be traced back to Jacob in 1930 B.C. which
nobody doubts, then it is entirely reasonable and scientific
to trace the entire human race back to Noah and his family

in 2519 B.C. Of course this proves nothing as to the date of *Adam's* creation; but if the Bible figures are shown to be correct as far back as Noah, then there is no good reason to doubt their accuracy for the previous 1,700 years.

Now let us examine the evolutionary hypothesis. If we push back the date of our ancestors by as little at 1,600 years (and deny the fact of the Flood, as evolutionists do), we must multiply the present world population by $2^{10} =$ 1,024, more than a thousandfold! If we double that time (3,200) and add it to 2519 B.C. (thus postulating 5719 B.C. as the birthday of *homo sapiens*), then the present population would be one million times as great as it is today. And remember, we are basing this on a rate of growth very much slower than that which is going on all round us now (doubling in about 40 years). But evolutionists would have us believe that man has been on the earth not a mere 7,000 years, but 7,000,000! in which case there would be "standing room only" on every square inch of the surface of the globe, including the Sahara desert and the North and South Poles. Truly this is 'reductio ad absurdum".

To sum up the case for the prosecution:

(1) Absolutely no proof exists for the physical connection of any hominid, ape-man, or "missing-link", with the present human race. Human remains are as old or older than any of them.

(2) Among the fossils supposed by evolutionists to be older than man, none has ever been discovered which could "connect" man with the lower mammals.

(3) Historical records of any human civilisation before 4000 B.C. are completely absent. When real man does appear he is astonishingly "sapiens" (wise): mentally and physically in no way inferior to 20th century space-men.

(4) Population statistics prove beyond a shadow of

doubt that to reckon the age of man in hundreds of thousands of years is hopelessly, not to say ludicrously, unscientific.

We may therefore conclude that the Bible account of man's creation out of the dust of the ground some 6,000 years ago may be literally, historically, and scientifically true. For no demonstrable scientific fact so far known (without assumptions) can contradict that date.[1]

[1]For more recent investigation on dating fossils etc. see Chapter 17.

CHAPTER 14

THE POPULARITY OF EVOLUTION

It was through the writings of Buffon and others in the latter half of the 18th century that the world was prepared to accept the present theory of evolution. Charles Lyell in 1830 published his book *Principles of Geology* which encouraged Charles Darwin to publish his famous book *Origin of Species* in 1859. After the publication of this book, the idea of organic evolution spread like wildfire, and caught the imagination of all intellectuals. This new concept soon revolutionised the very thinking of man and had significant repercussions on the life and morals of all Western civilisation. Though eminent scientists like Adam Sedgwick (Darwin's teacher) took exception to many of Darwin's statements, the majority of scientists and the general public accepted the theory of evolution by Natural Selection as a proven fact.

Now its tenets have so permeated human life and thought, that anyone who opposes the theory of evolution is taken to be an enemy of science and human progress. He is dubbed an obscurantist! Even publicity agents like newspapers and the B.B.C. refuse to publish anything against the evolutionary concept. But do all scientists agree that evolution is true?

Charles Darwin himself, the father of Evolution, in his later days gradually became aware of the lack of real evidence for his evolutionary speculation and wrote: "As by this theory, innumerable transitional forms must have existed.

Why do we not find them embedded in the crust of the earth? Why is not all nature in confusion instead of being, as we see them, well defined species?" This is why Darwin recanted towards the end of his life, as reported elsewhere in this volume (Appendix). After a century of research his ardent supporters like H. H. Newman are forced to confess: "Reluctant as he may be, honesty compels the evolutionist to admit, that there is no absolute proof of organic evolution."

Louis Agassiz, late Professor of Harvard University says: "The theory (of evolution) is a scientific mistake . . . there is not a fact known to Science tending to show that any being in the natural process of reproduction and multiplication has ever diverged from the course natural to its kind, or that a single kind has ever been transmuted into any other" (quoted already – 1860).

William Bateson, F.R.S., of Cambridge University: "We no longer feel, as we used to, that the process of variation now contemporaneously occurring is the beginning of a work which needs merely the element of time for its completion; for even time cannot complete that which has not begun."

Professor R. Goldschmidt of the University of California: "The statement of the problem already indicates that I cannot agree with the view-point of the text books, that the problem of evolution has been solved as far as the genetic basis is concerned. . . . Nowhere have the limits of the species been transgressed and these limits are separated from the limits of the next good species by the unabridged gap, which also includes sterility." Sir William Dawson, Professor of Geology: "There is no direct evidence that in the course of geological time one species has been gradually or suddenly changed into another."

Dr. A. H. Clark of the U.S. National Museum, Washington: "Thus, so far as concerns the major groups of animals, the creationist seems to have the better of the argument. There is not the slightest evidence that any one of the major groups arose from any other, each is a special animal complex, related more or less closely to all the rest, and appearing, therefore, as a special and distinct creation."

Regarding the evolution of man, he says: "Every bone in the body of man is at once distinguishable from the corresponding bone in the body of any of the apes. Man is not an ape and in spite of similarity between them, there is not the slightest evidence that man is descended from an ape."

Dr. George Gaylord Simpson of the American Museum of Natural History: "In the early days of evolutionary palaeontology it was answered that the major groups would be filled in by further discoveries, and even falsely, that some discoveries had already filled them. As it becomes more and more evident that the great gaps remained, despite wonderful progress in finding the members of lesser transitional groups and progressive lines, it was no longer satisfactory to impute this absence of objective data entirely to chance."

G. K. Hobbert, British Entomologist: "The evidence of fossils very definitely favours creation and not the evolution theory. The evolution theory bristles with anatomical and biochemical difficulties."

Professor John M. Coulter of the University of Chicago: "The variations which have occurred . . . produce species of the same phylogenetic level or declining in rank. There is as yet no adequate explanation of progressive evolution, the advance from one great phylum to another."

Professor W. R. Thompson, F.R.S., Director of the Commonwealth Institute of Biological Control, who wrote the introduction to the latest (1963) edition of *Origin of Species:* "The concept of organic evolution is very highly prized by biologists, for many of whom it is an object of genuinely religious devotion, because they regard it as a supreme interpretative principle. This is probably the reason why the severe methodical criticism employed in other departments of biology has not yet been brought to bear against evolutionary speculation. There are, however, indications that this criticism will not now be long delayed."

Professor Frank Allen of the University of Manitoba: "According to the theory of evolution, there should be a progressive building up from the simplest, hydrogen, to the most complex, uranium. The exact opposite, however, is found. Uranium is known to disintegrate into a series of elements of diminishing weights, the most sensational of which is radium, and the final one is lead. During this process, atoms of the gas helium, the next lightest to hydrogen, are thrown off. The heaviest elements are therefore the origin of the lightest."

No evidence of any kind in physics, chemistry or astronomy supports the theory of evolution. Among Botanists, Zoologists, Palaeontologists, Geneticists, etc., there are a number of first-rate scientists and research workers who do not believe in the theory of evolution. The same may be said of scientists in other fields, such as physics, chemistry, biochemistry and astronomy. This is why Arthur N. Field, a journalist of New Zealand, made the following statement: "What is it (evolution) based upon? Upon nothing whatever but faith, upon belief in the reality of the unseen – belief in the fossils that cannot be produced, belief in the embryological evidence that does not exist, belief in the breeding experiments that refuse to come off. It is faith unjustified by works."

CHAPTER 15

EVOLUTION AND CIVILISATION

It has been the privilege of the writer to expose the utter bankruptcy of the arguments in favour of the theory of evolution. The steady accumulation of scientific facts wholly opposed to this theory have become so great that the theory has now to rest upon faith and not on scientific facts as was once supposed – faith in the reality of the unseen. That is "belief in the fossils which cannot be produced, belief in the embryological evidence that does not exist, and belief in the breeding experiments that refuse to come off".

Because it is not founded on facts, the theory of evolution carries with it a philosophy of life which runs contrary to all that is right and noble in human nature – a philosophy that extinguishes the very light of human reason and faith. The late Professor Adam Sedgwick, author of the famous *Student's Text Book of Zoology*, after reading the book, *The Origin of Species*, expressed his opinion to Darwin in the following words: "I have read your book with more pain than pleasure. Parts of it I admired greatly, parts I laughed till my sides were almost sore: other parts I read with absolute sorrow because I think them utterly false and grievously mischievous." As feared by this great man of science, the evolutionary idea of civilisation, far from being a scientific abstraction, has grown into a practical method of thought and code of conduct, affecting the reasonings and actions of every part of the human race. Human conduct is

95

modelled on the philosophy that finds current acceptance. Professor J. Holmes, in *Science* (14th August, 1939, p. 117) says: "Few people who accept the Darwinian theory of evolution realise its far-reaching import especially in Social Science." Of the many evils that have resulted from the teaching of evolution, we mention only a few.

In the first place the theory of evolution has given to human society a new code of ethics replacing the divine law of love and service. In *Science* (1939, p. 121) Professor J. Holmes says, "Darwinism consistently applied would measure goodness in terms of survival value", and again, "Fundamentally, therefore, our ethics are Darwinian whether we like it or not". This is the law of the jungle where "might is right" and the fittest survive. Whether cunning or cruelty, cowardice or deceit, whatever will enable the individual to survive is good and right for that individual or that society. According to this Darwinian hypothesis, Huxley held that "it was cunning and ruthlessness that enabled man to evolve from the beasts". And again: "It is this law of the jungle that has to be the directive for all so-called human progress!" Is it a wonder then that this principle of evolution has undermined all that is beautiful and worthy in human nature? It is this perverse way of thinking that has been responsible for the increase of crime among the youth of today. It will not be out of place, in this connection, to cite an incident that actually took place in the city of Chicago in the year 1924.

In defending two young men, Loeb and Leopold, for cruelly murdering a fourteen-year-old boy, by name Bobby Franks, the celebrated criminal lawyer of the day, Clarence Darrow, traced their crime back to what they had learned in the university. He argued: "Is there any blame attached because somebody took Nietzsche's philosophy seriously?" His appeal to the judge was, "Your honour, it is hardly fair to hang a nineteen-year-old boy for the philosophy that was taught him at the university" – (From *Classified Speeches*, edited by W. Brigans). No

wonder that Brigadier General F. D. Frost stated in the
Fundamentalist, January 1950, page 21, "There is no doubt
about it that the doctrine of evolution is the greatest curse
in our educational system". Whether we read Ward's
Dynamic Sociology, or Russell's *Ostrich Code of Morals* or
Briffault's *Immoralism* or any other book written by the
Behaviorist School, they all seem to endeavour to justify
and base their conclusions on the bestial nature of man.
This philosophy seeks to undermine the morale, the
principles and practice of virtuous conduct and to reduce
man to the level of animal nature. The surging unrest, the
broken homes, the frustrated lives, the increasing divorce
cases, the multiplied number of criminals are but the
inevitable outcome of the acceptance and practice of this
evolutionary doctrine. Needless to say, this concept is
diametrically opposed to the noble and divine law of Christ,
"By love serve one another".

Secondly, it must be admitted that evolution is the basic
principle on which Militarism is founded. The great German
exponent of Militarism, Nietzsche, extended the Darwinian
principle of the survival of the fittest in order to inspire his
countrymen to fight. According to him, "The supreme
standard of life is purely materialistic vitality and power to
survive". The 1914-1918 war was thus the calculated climax
of a policy nourished on the diabolical ideas of Nietzsche
for the subjugation of the world. General Von Bernhardi
in his book, *The Next War*, shows the connection between
war and biology. According to him, "War is a biological
necessity of the first importance, a regulative element in the
life of mankind that cannot be dispensed with. War increases vitality, and promotes human progress". The
summum bonum of life according to Nietzsche's own words is
"Man shall be trained for war and women for the recreation
of the warrior; all else is folly". (*Complete Works of Nietzsche*,
Oscar Levy, sixth edition 1930, vol II, p. 75.) Adolph Hitler
reiterated the same philosophy of life derived from the
theory of evolution when he said, "The whole of nature is

a continuous struggle between strength and weakness, an eternal victory of the strong over the weak". He took the doctrine of evolution seriously and applied it to the progress of his own nation. According to him the German race with its superior intellect and Aryan blood was the best fitted to survive and dominate the world. But, alas, his shameful defeat in 1945 demonstrated to the world that his philosophy was a lie, and proved the truthfulness of God's Word, as it is written in Ecclesiastes 9: 11, "The race is not to the swift nor the battle to the strong".

A third disastrous result of the impact of the theory of evolution on human society is the universal spread of atheism among the educated masses. Thousands of young men and women have lost their faith in God as a result of studying the theory of evolution. The outcome of the theory was foreseen by Professor Huxley who had a mind well trained in logical reasoning, for he said, "The doctrine of evolution, if consistently accepted, makes it impossible to believe the Bible". This theory leads one, consciously or unconsciously, to a state of defiance against God as Creator and Redeemer. Evolution thus becomes a cornerstone of atheism. The President of the American Association for the Advancement of Atheism, Mr. Charles Smith, said in his *Annual Report* in 1928, page 15, that "Evolution is Atheism". Evolution and Christianity are incompatibles. If evolution is true the whole fabric of Christian faith is a mass of error. There was no creation and there was no fall. Consequently there is no need for redemption and there is none to redeem. Man evolves from a speck of protoplasm ever progressing towards a higher goal, culminating in the formation of the superman. In this process of evolution a fallen nature is unthinkable. According to Nietzsche, "Neither crime, cruelty, sexuality, nor intoxication need be matters of shame or repentance". To him Christian morality was the principal obstacle to the emergence of a superman. Yet there are so many Christians who seem to believe in the theory of evolution as well as in the God of the Bible. However, in the

minds of atheists there is no doubt regarding the outcome
of the theory of evolution. The Vice-President of the
American Association for the Advancement of Atheism,
Mr. Woolsey Teller, in his pamphlet, *Evolution implies
Atheism*, stated: "The God idea cannot be reconciled with
our knowledge of evolution." Newman Watts, the London
journalist, was right when he said, "Every attack on the
Christian faith made today has as its basis the doctrine of
evolution" – (from the pamphlet, *This is Serious*).

A fourth disastrous effect is the spread of communism.
Communists like Fascists, used Darwinism. Frederick Engel
wrote to Karl Marx in 12th December, 1859, "Darwin
whom I am just now reading is splendid". Karl Marx in
reply wrote "Although it is developed in crude English
style, this is the book which contains the basis in natural
history for our views". (See Zirkle Conway, 1959 – *Evolution, Marxian Biology and Social Science*, p. 85.) Marx wished
to dedicate to Darwin his book *Das Kapital*, but Darwin
politely declined the offer. It is not only the founders of
Communism that were influenced by Darwin but also men
like Joseph Stalin were much influenced by him. Yeroslovasky, a friend of Joseph Stalin, wrote, "At a very early
stage, while still a pupil in the Ecclesiastical school, Comrade
Stalin developed a critical mind and revolutionary senti-
ments. He began to read Darwin and became an atheist".[1]

[1] E. Yeroslovasky, 1940. *Landmarks in the life of Stalin* – page 8 (Adapted from
C.S.R. 1969, Vol. 5, No. 4, p. 152.)

CHAPTER 16

EVOLUTION
AND CHRISTIANITY

From the foregoing chapters of this book, it has been made clear that although many scientists still cling to the theory of evolution, hoping somehow to find ways and means of supporting the theory, yet evolution as conceived by Charles Darwin is contradicted by the facts. The great geneticist Heribert Nilsson who had spent more than forty years of his life in trying to investigate the problem of Speciation, has put it: "Investigations over the last three decades into the problem of the origin of species have not been able to show that a variational material capable of competition in the struggle for existence is formed by mutation." Even accepting it as an article of faith, we have seen the disastrous fruits it has produced upon the life and conduct of both man and society. Unlike its counterpart, namely the doctrine of creation, evolution gave the wrong code of ethics to mankind. It has also encouraged militarism and atheism through the law of the jungle. Foreseeing such an outcome Professor Huxley said: "The doctrine of evolution is directly antagonistic to that of creation. Evolution consistently accepted makes it impossible to believe the Bible." This is a true evaluation of facts, and truly there can be no real reconciliation between Darwin's theory of evolution and the central doctrine of the Bible. Evolution not only contradicts the record of creation in the Bible but also goes counter to the basic principles on which Christianity is founded. Evolution teaches the bestial origin of man and his gradual progress to perfect manhood with the passage of time. The Bible, on the other hand, teaches that man was created as a perfect being, in the very image of God, and that through sin he became degraded, necessitating his redemption through the death of Jesus Christ on the cross. Which is true? If evolution is true there was no fall and no need for redemption, for man is gradually evolving into a superman.

If evolution is true, there was no creation, no fall, no redemption and Christ died in vain. Thus the most essential doctrines of Christianity, including the atonement, are done away with. This is what made Mr. R. Blatchford, editor of an infidel paper *Clarion*, say, "The Bible declares that God created the heavens and the earth. But he who heartily accepts the theory of evolution believes all this to be untrue. The Bible declares that God created man in the likeness of His own image. But he who heartily accepts the theory of evolution believes that this is untrue. What kind of a religious belief can that be, which is helped by the theory of evolution?"

In Universities where Christianity and evolution are taught, the outcome has been to produce "Theistic Evolutionists". They seem to believe that God allowed the universe to evolve slowly out of a "nebula" and thus the sun, earth, and planets were formed. By their view God did not create instantaneously by the word of His mouth, as recorded in Genesis. They also believe that man came into being by a slow process of evolution from a bit of protoplasm, passing through various progressive changes and finally emerging out of a beast like the ape. Some years ago a doctor of Zoology wrote an article in a "Christian" magazine suggesting that God chose the best pair of apes and breathed into them and they became "living souls". On enquiry we learned that the writer was a "fundamentalist" and a "literalist" who believed in the fall and the need for redemption through atonement. If his thesis were true, the question may naturally be asked what happened to the other evolving pairs of apes? Did they evolve into soulless men and women? As far as science knows there never was a race of men without a soul; even the aborigines worship a God and are different from apes. No! Theistic Evolution and Bible Christianity cannot be satisfactorily reconciled. Christianity is a revelation from God and not the highest product of human imagination or intuition. God has spoken to man through various prophets of old, and in these last days through His Son, Jesus Christ. The Bible tells us that it is the same Spirit of Christ that spoke through prophets of old. There is therefore no contradiction between what those prophets wrote and what Christ said.

THE IMPORTANCE OF THE DOCTRINE OF CREATION
FOR A CHRISTIAN

(1) *The doctrine of creation is important for the Christian view of marriage.*

Jesus said: "Have ye not read that He which made them at the beginning made them male and female, and said, For this cause shall a man leave his father and mother, and shall cleave unto his wife: and they shall be one flesh?" And again "from the beginning it (i.e. divorce) was not so" (Matthew 19: 4-8). St. Paul in 1 Timothy 2: 13 tells us how Adam was first formed and then Eve; and in 1 Corinthians 11: 8 he refers even to the manner in which woman was created. "For the man is not of (out of) the woman, but the woman is of (out of) the man." It is clear from these quotations that Jesus Christ and His apostles upheld the literal truth of the creation story as recorded in Genesis, *and upon it based all their teaching* about marriage, namely:

(a) The supreme importance of the marriage tie – more important even than duty towards one's parents. Adam and Eve had no parents!

(b) The permanence of the marriage tie: one man for one woman for life.

(c) The spiritual meaning of the marriage tie: they shall be one flesh because they *were* one flesh literally and physically.

Surely it is significant that the teaching of Evolution in Schools and Colleges in the last fifty years has coincided (at least in Western countries) with a staggering rise in the divorce rate and a flood of immorality among teenagers. Teach a young man that he is related to the baboon, and you can scarcely blame him for sexual promiscuity.

(2) *The doctrine of creation is important for the Christian view of society and man's duty to his neighbour.*

Jesus Christ taught that it is the meek – not the aggressive – who shall inherit the earth; that it is the poor – not the rich – who are blessed; that he who loves his life shall lose it, and he who loses his life shall find it. Historically it is a fact that only Christianity has taught man to care for "useless" old people (instead of strangling them, as some tribes of North America used to); and to bring up "unwanted" girl babies, instead of putting them out to die. All these doctrines and practices are flatly opposed to evolution with its vaunted "progress" through the survival of the fittest.

(3) *The doctrine of creation is important for the Christian attitude to prayer.*

Theistic Evolution pushes God back into the dateless past, admits that He can forgive sin and answer "spiritual" prayers, but denies (or at least is *prone to forget*) that God even now breaks into His own universe to do things that otherwise would remain undone, in answer to His children's prayers. To the evolutionist everything is a miracle and nothing is a miracle. The walls of Jericho falling down "supernaturally" was no more marvellous than a raindrop falling down "naturally". Thus the nerve of vital prayer is cut and Christians resign themselves to a feeble fatalism instead of looking to God concerning the work of His hands (Isaiah 45: 11).

(4) *The doctrine of creation is important in relation to the
     Second Coming of our Lord Jesus Christ.*

Theistic Evolutionists picture the creation of all things as
having taken place in the very remote past, and easily slip
into thinking that the consummation of all things may take
place in the very remote future. So there is no urgent need
to evangelise the world or to "prepare to meet thy God".
Belief in the theory of evolution leads to disbelief in the
authority of Revelation. As Professor Marcus Dods has
written: "If the *days* of Genesis, chapter 1, do not mean
literal days of 24 hours, then all exegesis of the Bible is
hopeless."

The consistent Creationist, on the other hand, pictures
himself as on a train running between two fixed points.
It started at a definite place and at a definite time – not so far
distant; it is rapidly approaching a definite *terminus;* and all
passengers must be ready to meet the Prime Minister!

(5) *The doctrine of creation is important for the Christian view
     of heaven.*

The Evolutionist lives only in the present. He cannot
conceive of a world that was ever different from this one in
the past, nor of a world that will ever be different from this
one in the future. To him "all things continue as they were
from the beginning". To the questions: Why are there
microbes and disease? Why floods and tornadoes? Why is
nature "red in tooth and claw?" Above all, why does

>   "Man's inhumanity to man
>   Make countless thousands mourn?"

His answer is blank agnosticism. There is no answer; there
is no remedy; there is no hope. But the Bible answer is
clear, challenging, thrilling. God made the earth perfect:
there were no microbes or diseases, no floods or tornadoes,
and probably even no carnivores, in the dawn of creation.
"And God saw everything that He had made, and behold, it
was very good." But the earth as we see it today lies *under
a curse* because of our sin. "The whole creation groaneth

and travaileth in pain together until now." Yet the great God who laid this curse is able also to lift it: there shall come a day when "the wolf shall dwell with the lamb, and the leopard shall lie down with the kid, and a little child shall lead them. The lion shall eat straw like the ox . . . they shall not hurt nor destroy in all my holy mountain".

CHAPTER 17

MODERN METHODS OF DATING AND BIBLE CHRONOLOGY

The author of this book has found it easy to refute the arguments in favour of the theory of evolution and show their bankruptcy in the light of modern facts of science. Since it was first published in 1966, more facts have come to light that so tilted the balance definitely against the theory of evolution, that many scientists and liberal theologians have begun to have second thoughts on the theory. In a letter recently received by the writer, an eminent British Scientist wrote, "I think that scientists in England are having second thoughts on evolution but in America they seem set on it". As our knowledge increases, support for the theory of evolution seems to be disappearing.

However, one aspect of the theory, namely the time factor, continued to puzzle the writer. Believing as he does in the record of creation described in the first chapter of the Bible, he found it almost impossible to reconcile a recent creation of the earth with the millions of years usually attributed to the age of the earth, sun, moon and stars. As a school boy, he was taught that the stars are millions of "light years" away from the earth and light from only some of the stars has so far reached the earth inspite of light travelling at the rate of 186,000 miles per second. Also he was told that light from more distant stars has not yet reached the earth. Rightly or wrongly he believed that the earth was at least a few million years old having received light from some of the distant stars. This idea was set at the back of his mind, and his studies on the geological ages in evolution only confirmed his conviction about the great age of the earth. For he once believed, along with other evolutionists, that such eons of time were an absolute necessity for the evolution of the universe and all things therein. The dependence of the evolutionist on time is so great that George Wald (1955)[1] says "Time is in fact the hero of the plot. . . . Given so much time, the impossible becomes possible, the possible probable, and the probable virtually certain. One has only to wait: time itself performs miracles". Accordingly, thousands of miracles can happen in succession for anything to evolve into anything else provided time is inexhaustible. This is the illogical philosophy of the evolutionist which does not demand any evidence.

The Bible on the other hand demands acceptance of a world whose time is measured and destined to end at the completion of God's purpose. There is thus a conflict between the time envisaged for creation of heaven and earth and all things in them as stated in the Bible (Genesis 1 and Exodus 20: 11) and the limitless time postulated by evolutionists. Either the Bible is right or the assumption of the evolutionists is right regarding the concept of time. This challenge of evolution thus compels every student of science and theology to face up to the Bible chronology. Bible chronology being fixed, the only way open to us is to re-examine the modern scientific methods of dating. We must re-examine scientifically the modern methods of dating in the light of Bible chronology.

DATING OF ROCKS, FOSSILS ETC.

There are various "time-clocks" proposed and used by scientists to find out the age of rocks, fossils and other artifacts. All these time-clocks can be classified into two groups, the *quantitative* and the *qualitative*. The quantitative clocks help in determining the actual age of the material while the qualitative only indicate greater or lesser age without actual determination of years. Of the quantitative clocks only two remain in scientific favour today, namely the Radio-carbon method and the Potassium-argon method. Other methods there are which involve many assumptions which are shaky and each contingent on the previous assumption.

Of the qualitative time-clocks many positively point to a relatively recent origin of matter and not a single one can be found to establish the evolutionary scales of time or the order of the geologic ages. They do not even refute the Bible.

This dilemma made the evolutionist cling desperately to the faith that Radio-carbon and Potassium-argon or some other new time-clock can be made to support his theory. But when we look carefully at the basic constants and assumptions in the Radio-carbon method, we find that it not only confirms Biblical history but also points unmistakably to a Biblical creation. The Potassium-argon clock is meaningless unless one assumes a creation date. In short (as Rober L. Whitelaw says in *Creation Research Society*[2]), "neither one of these much-quoted time-clocks is found to establish the date of any rock, fossil or artifact beyond the date of Biblical creation, namely 5000 B.C.". Though the Bible does not establish a definite creation date, it indicates that the time of creation is the time of the creation of the first man and woman delineated with clarity in Genesis chapters 5 and 11. We may therefore take it as 5000 B.C.

THE CARBON-14 TIME-CLOCK

The writer has already explained Carbon C^{14} method of dating in chapter 3 of this book under "The Age of the earth", pages 20-23. Since this book was first published much research work was done in many parts of the world which thoroughly revolutionised the dates once assigned to fossils etc. It was found that both the production rate

of Radio-carbon and the decaying rate once assumed by
W. F. Libby had to be abandoned.

More than 100 Radio-carbon laboratories had been
established in the world by 1968 and only about 15,000
dates of various ancient materials have so far been recorded.
Of these 15,000 dates, all except three do not exceed 50,000
years. And the three exceptions out of the 15,000 dates are
stated as "infinite". The fact is, radio-activity from specimens
older than 50,000 years is scarcely detectable in a Geiger
Counter. It is surprising to note that if Lyellian geology and
evolutionary time are valid and if living matter on earth had
been accumulating over eons of time, then millions of
undatable materials should have been present on the earth.
Yet, the materials so far dated, be these from Babylon, India
or other ancient countries, were all found datable within
50,000 years, though they went to the maximum depth of
any deposit. Thus all datable radio-carbon activity, even
carboniferous strata (100,000,000 years), was within 50,000
years. Yet scientists using evolutionary premises, had
assigned such ancient material to ages well beyond 100,000
and even millions of years, while actual dates scientifically
recorded are only in thousands. Mastodon, Mylodon,
Sabretooth tiger, were all dated from 10,000 to 30,000 years
including Neanderthal man, Heidelburg man, Zinjathropus
and Australopithecus etc. Deep ocean deposits came within
40,000 years. Further it is evident that the most ancient
dates of human culture are found in the Near East, and the
oldest "human" dates in the western hemisphere are
historically younger.

But even the above dates when corrected for the basic
scientific error evident in Libby's experiment not only point
to a recent creation but also show an unmistakable world-
wide disappearance of man and animals for a long period
about 5,000 years ago. This seems to indicate a world-wide
catastrophe like the Biblical flood. However, the evolutionary concept of time certainly stands wholly discredited. For
details of recent Radio-carbon dating method, the reader's

attention is drawn to an article in the *Creation Research Society*.[3] Only the conclusions arrived at by the author of this article are herewith quoted.

Rober L. Whitelaw, Professor of Nuclear and Mechanical Engineering, Virginia Polytechnic Institute, after investigating about 15,000 radio-carbon dates so far published by various scientists all over the world and correcting them for the basic scientific errors and computing them backwards and classifying them, gave the following conclusions:

(1) "Radio-carbon supports the idea of Biblical creation by pointing unmistakably to a recent beginning of cosmic radiation.

(2) Radio-carbon supports a date of creation at approximately 7000 B.P. (Before Present).

(3) Radio-carbon supports the contemporaneous appearance of all forms of living matter at creation. Man and modern animals, along with extinct flora and fauna all appear equally ancient and with equal suddenness.

(4) Radio-carbon supports the beginning of the human race from a few ancestors in the vicinity of the Near East.

(5) Radio-carbon, on the other hand, indicates the sudden concurrent appearance of the rest of the animal kingdom in larger numbers in every part of the world.

(6) Radio-carbon clearly indicates an original world in which both trees and low-lying vegetation were profuse and wide-spread even throughout the present polar regions and deserts. (Facts amply attested by geology and paleontology of an ancient world uniquely different in climate, in location and elevation of the very continents and possibly even in the inclination of the earth's axis!)

(7) Radio-carbon points to some drastic change, shortly after creation, which depleted both animal world

and arboreal vegetation but without noticeable effect upon the multiplication of man, just such an effect as might be deduced from Genesis 3.

(8) Radio-carbon clearly points to a world-wide catastrophe destructive of man, beast and tree, just as described in Genesis 7 and confirmed elsewhere in Scripture, in world-wide human tradition, and in world-wide geological evidence.

(9) Radio-carbon supports the dates of such a catastrophe at about 4950 B.P.

(10) Radio-carbon indicates a large and widespread human population in the world just before its catastrophe.

(11) Radio-carbon indicates the wide spread existence of now-extinct flora and fauna in the world before this catastrophe, including evidence of the gradual extinction of many forms during the two millenia between it and creation.

(12) Radio-carbon indicates that the 're-origin' of both animals and man after this catastrophe was in the vicinity of the Near East and noticeably later in the western hemisphere.

(13) Radio-carbon supports the Biblical chronology of ancient empires and of Israel and exposes suspected exaggerations in Manetho, Berosus *et al.*

(14) Finally, there is no question as to which concept of time and history is supported by the radio-carbon record. Is it the endless time and meaningless history postulated by evolution? Or is it a specific span of time marked off by the purposeful acts of a sovereign God, from creation to flood, to cross, to ultimate consummation, as the Bible portrays?

Fifteen thousand radio-carbon dates, dead voices from the past assembled by scientists from every kind of once-living matter and every corner of the globe, now answer the question unequivocally in favour of the Bible!"

POTASSIUM ARGON TIME-CLOCK

The other quantitative time-clock is the Potassium argon time-clock. Finding practically little support for the geological ages in the Radio-carbon clock, scientists have now turned to the second time-clock, namely the Potassium argon time-clock. This method of dating is extensively dealt with by Schaeffer and Zahringer.[4] The concept is basically simple except that it involves a thoroughly unscientific assumption which nullifies the whole method. Since Potassium-bearing rocks are plentiful in the earth's crust, this time-clock seemed handy to verify the billions of years postulated by Evolutionary geology. There are only two problems to be solved: (1) How to measure the fantastically small quantities of argon trapped in the rock specimen? and (2) how to determine what portion of this argon in all those billions of years, came from potassium decay, and what portion came from the earth's atmosphere where, unfortunately it is very plentiful (almost 1 per cent by volume)? Here also big assumptions had to be made. Argon-38, one of the isotopic distribution in atmospheric argon, is dismissed as too small to be detected. Again, a big assumption is that the ratio of Ar-36 to Ar-40 in the atmosphere *has remained exactly the same as it was the day the rock was formed*. These are nullified by other scientific facts which indicate that Argon-36 is a probable product of cosmic radiation bombarding the earth's outer space just as is radio-carbon. From such calculations the date of a rock cannot be determined until one first assumes a date of creation and a date of building up of Argon-36 in the air thereafter.

The nature and magnitude of error in such calculations may be estimated from the following example. Dr. Hallonquist in the *Journal of Geophysical Research*[5] reports that the lava rocks formed in 1800 and 1801 in Hualalai, Hawaii, show an age of 160 million to three billion years by the Potassium-argon dating method, although these rocks are well known to be no more than 174 years old. Similar reports from Germany, Norway, France, Russia, etc. are pouring in, showing that Potassium-argon and Uranium-lead radioactive dating methods have been used to give ages of millions and billions of years to rocks that are known to be only a few hundred years old. Thus both these time-clocks are not dependable.

From the above facts of science recently gathered from various countries it is clear that of the two popular scientific methods of dating rocks, fossils or other artifacts, the Potassium-argon method is totally unreliable because of the great assumptions that have to be taken. On the other hand the Carbon-14 method when corrected according to the data made available to science, seems to point not only to a recent creation of the universe, about 7,000 years ago, but also confirms the chronology of the Bible, indicating the probable date of a world-wide catastrophe like the Genesis flood. For if the death dates gathered from all parts of the globe were to be distributed by age, by location and by type in accordance with an ancient historical record like that of the Bible, there is an anomaly which cannot be explained easily. For instance, there is a marked drop-off of death dates about 5,000 years ago (before the present) which exactly corresponds to the world-wide catastrophe or the Genesis flood described in the Bible. This catastrophe at such a time has been amply attested by competent writers like Professor McReady Price, Dr. Morris etc.

In this connection, it may be profitable for us to consider other evidence from archaeology and population statistics which establish the modernity of man and refute the evolutionary concept of time and history. For this the attention of the reader is directed to the writer's previous comments.[6] According to Arnold J. Toynbee "The first appearance of the species (human) was about 6,000 years ago". It is a fact that no records of any ancient civilisation go back beyond 3000 B.C. except what is recorded in the Bible. Egyptian, Babylonian and Chinese culture and civilisation do not go beyond 3000 B.C. Note-worthy also is the fact that civilisations spring into view *suddenly*.

W. F. Libby N.L. nuclear physicist says in *Science*,[7] "Arnold (a co-worker) and I had our first shock when our advisers informed us that history extended back only for 5,000 years . . . in fact the earliest historical date that has been established with any degree of certainty is about the time of the first Dynasty in Egypt". *The World Book Encyclopedia* 1966, Vol. 6, page 12 says, "The earliest records we have of human history go back only about 5,000 years". Again the *Encyclopedia Americana* says, "Social Evolution in man, however, has occupied not more than 10,000 years. Most of it has happened in the last 6,000 years".[8] *Biology for Today*, page 327 says concerning the age of metals, "The era began about 5,000 years ago and extends to our present day". In *The Man: His First Million Years*[9] we read: "The earliest written language, Sumerian cuneiform, goes back to about 3500 B.C." These are facts shown to us. But evolutionists contend that man advanced more rapidly in the last 6,000 years than he did in the million or more years of his prehistoric existence![10] Dr. P. T. Wiseman in his *New Discoveries in Babylonia about Genesis*[11] says, "No more surprising fact has been discovered by recent excavation than the suddenness with which civilisation appeared in the world. This discovery is the very opposite to that anticipated" (by evolutionists). It was expected the more ancient the period, the more primitive would excavators find it to be, until traces of civilisations ceased altogether and aboriginal man appeared. Neither in Babylonia nor Egypt, the lands of the oldest habitations of man, has this been the case.

Contrary to the popular belief, the brain capacity of the ancients was highly developed according to a discovery in Iraq. *New York Times*[12] says that, "mathematics reached a stage of development about 2000 B.C. that archaeologists and historians of science had never imagined possible". In fact, some of the cultures degenerated into the "stone age", as we can see today in New Guinea, Africa and some parts

of Australia. According to *Science's Year* reporting on a
conference of Anthropologists,[13] "Many of the so-called
primitive peoples of the world today, most of the par-
ticipants agreed, may not be so primitive after all. They
suggested that certain hunting tribes in Africa, Central
India, South America, and the Western Pacific are not
relics of the stone age, as has been previously thought, but
instead are the 'wreckage' of more highly developed
societies forced through various circumstances to lead a
much simpler, less developed life". Thus the so called
primitive people are not in the process of evolution but in
the process of degeneration. This process of degeneration is
even described by Job in one of the oldest books of the
Bible.[14]

The same testimony is borne from the study of languages.
According to evolutionists it took ages for the evolution of
modern languages from the series of grunts with which
primitive men expressed themselves. Dr. Mason, specialist
on American languages found as per *Science News Letter*,[15]
"Evolution in language is just the opposite of biological
evolution. Languages have evolved from the complex to the
simple". The above facts only revealed what is stated in the
Bible that man was *created* with the power of speech and
the gift of a perfect language which later on got degenerated
into our modern simple languages during the last six to
seven thousand years. This view seems to be in agreement
with modern discoveries. Thus man's existence on earth
cannot be proved to be more than six to seven thousand
years through facts of science or history.

Another line of argument is drawn from population
statistics. Statisticians agree that about 150 years is a reasonable average for the human race to double its numbers,
when allowance has been made for wars, famines etc. But
the Bible has given a more accurate method of determining
the doubling rate. The details of calculation are worked out
in the chapter titled *Evolution and Man*.[16] Both from the
Jewish population from Jacob's marriage in 1930 B.C. to

A.D. 1930, and from Noah's flood to the world population in 1965, it is shown that the doubling rate of the entire human race has been once every 160 years. Examining the date of our ancestors from an evolutionary hypothesis (postulating even 5719 B.C. as the birthday of Homo sapiens), the present population would be one million times as great as it is today (denying the flood as evolutionists do and taking the doubling rate of 160 years).

Population statistics show that man has been on earth not more than 7,000 years. Thus to reckon his age on earth in hundreds of thousands of years seems to be hopelessly unscientific. It is not chronology but pure *guesseology*!

Such confirmation of the Bible chronology from the Carbon-14 method of dating and population statistics may be shocking to many scientists and even theologians. But the fact that Sir Isaac Newton, with all his knowledge of physics and astronomy, after independent calculations, saw nothing in astronomy to cause him to doubt a recent creation of about 6,000 years, should make every scientist and theologian pause and reconsider his preconceived ideas about Bible chronology and the veracity of the Word of God in general. As the Bible states in Exodus 20: 11 "In six days the Lord made heaven and earth, the sea and all that in them is, and rested on the seventh day".

This may not make sense to men like Professor G. G. Simpson (a great advocate of the theory of evolution), who do not see any divine purpose in this Universe. For he says the following:

"We cannot disprove the postulate that the universe was created one second ago, complete with all our apparent memories of our own earlier days, or that it was not created in 4004 B.C., with all the apparent record of earlier billions of years. But that would not make sense, and we must pretend, at least, that both we and the Universe are sane."[17]

But to the believer who believes that God created a functioning universe, out of nothing, and did not cause it to evolve out of a few atoms, it does make sense. Science does not disprove it. On the other hand many of the recent findings of science, point towards a recent creation.

SIX DAYS OF CREATION

These days do not seem to be "ages" or thousand-year periods as some would like to interpret. To the writer they are six days of 24 hours each with evenings and mornings leading up to the Sabbath on the seventh day. God did not create a *nabula* which in the course of millions of years evolved *into* the universe of today as per Laplace's hypothesis. Neither did He create a highly condensed core of protons and neutrons to expand themselves in five billion years into the present Universe as per George Gammouw's "Big Bang" theory. God does not perpetually bring into being a kind of background material like the atom Hydrogen to give rise to the matter of the universe as Professor Fred Hoyle of Cambridge once assumed and abandoned later. God did not create the universe in piecemeal. He created a functioning universe in six literal days of 24 hours – the work of creation of "Heaven and earth, the sea and all that in them is", which was finished in the first six days of creation about 7,000 years ago.

The Lord made light and darkness on the first day and on the second day He made the firmament. On the third day He made the Earth and the Seas, the earth bringing forth the grass and the fruit trees yielding fruit, each after its kind. Only on the fourth day did He make the holders of light like the sun and moon. He also made the stars on the same day. On the fifth day He created the moving creatures in the waters including whales, and the birds of the air, each after their kind. On the last day of His creation, He made the cattle, the beasts and the creeping creatures on the earth. His final act on the sixth day was the creation of Adam in His own image and Eve from his rib. After this He did not create anything new in Heaven or on Earth.

[1] In *The Origin of Life*, page 12.

[2] Quarterly, Vol. 5, No. 2, page 78.

[3] Quarterly vol. 7, No. 1, June 1970 by Robert L. Whitelaw entitled *Time, Life and History in the light of* 15,000 *Radio-carbon Dates*.

[4] *Potassium argon Dating*. Springer Verlag, New York, 1966.

[5] 15th July, 1968.

[6] Chapter 14, pages 86ff.

[7] 3rd March, 1961, page 1.

[8] *Encyclopedia Americana*, 1956, Vol. 10, page 613 b.

[9] Page 116.

[10] See *Biology and Human Progress* 1958, page 509 – Eisman and Tanger.

[11] 1949, page 28.

[12] 8th January, 1950, page 128.

[13] 1966, page 296.

[14] See Book of Job 30: 3-6.

[15] 3rd September, 1955, page 145.

[16] Pages 82-90.

[17] *The history of life* in the *Evolution of life*, sol tax. Ed. University of Chicago Press, 1960, page 175.

CHAPTER 18

CONCLUSION

After intense research for more than a century by qualified scientists in the field of biology, bringing to light many facts of science which contradict the assumptions of Darwin, the statement of Sir Arthur Keith that "Evolution is unproved and unprovable, we believe it because the only alternative is special creation, which is unthinkable" may now be restated as follows: "Evolution is unproved and now found to be untenable. We believe in creation because it was always the only possible alternative, and is now found to be more reasonable." In Sir James Jean's words, "Everything points with overwhelming force to a definite event or events of creation at some time or times not infinitely remote" (*Eos or The Wider Aspects of Cosmogeny*, p. 35).

Whether it be the study of cosmology, physics, chemistry, biology, biochemistry, geology or palaeontology, as far as the known facts of science are concerned, we are being compelled to uphold creation rather than evolution. It is no longer "creation", but "evolution" of one basic kind from another basic kind that is "unthinkable". It is no longer "Christianity" that is the principal obstacle of human progress but "evolution" that really hinders human progress. As Professor W. R. Thompson (Introduction to Darwin's *Origin of Species*, 1963 edition, p. 20), points out: "A great deal of this work (research work stimulated by Darwinism) was directed into unprofitable channels or devoted to the pursuit of will-o-the-wisps." The same author quotes D'Arcy Thompson's remark "on the *stultifying effect* of Darwinian theory". This apart, the social import of the concept of evolution has been disastrous and *unworkable*. We are therefore made to realise, that both for the progress of science and for the moral and spiritual progress of the human race, the earlier we abandon the philosophy of evolution, the better it will be for mankind.

THE REMEDY

The true remedy lies in completely abandoning the Darwinian conception of evolution and re-examining critically the facts of science with an unprejudiced mind, with a view to seeing whether they will fit into the only alternative doctrine, namely, the doctrine of "creation" as recorded in the Bible. This has been the attempt of the author ever since he had a spiritual experience as previously mentioned. Ever since that date (1931), the author has been studying the problem of evolution to see whether the facts of science in general, and zoology in particular, could be interpreted in terms of the biblical doctrine of creation. After personal investigation and examination of some of the original materials on which the theory of evolution was based, the author became convinced that scientific facts fit in better with the concept of creation than with evolution. Thus the doctrine of creation does not go counter to the established laws of thermodynamics. On the other hand it agrees with the principle of uncertainty and gives an adequate explanation for the origin of matter and life. It is also in harmony with the facts of palaeontology and genetics, giving ample scope for scientific research to discover the extent of variation within the basic kind created. The doctrine of creation does not lead to scientific speculation or falsification of scientific data in order to support a false theory. The concept of creation as stated in the Bible is not only in harmony with the latest facts of science but also promotes human progress in the right direction. It develops the complete man – his body, mind and also his spirit. It does not teach and lead men to the wrong "code of ethics" to fight and kill each other. It takes cognizance of his spiritual hunger which evolutionists ignore.

The concept of creation leads man to his Creator, and it satisfies the inner longings of his soul. For man is not an animal to be satisfied with the material things of the world. He is essentially a spiritual being. The Bible says that he was created "in the image of God". It was the Creator's breath breathed into him that made him "a living soul". The Bible also tells us that sin has marred that image of God in man. Nothing but the Creator's breath can restore that image back to him. The Psalmist says: "As the heart panteth after the water brooks, so panteth my heart after thee, O God." This very thirst in man's heart is an indication of the loving pull of his Creator. It is the same love that made this Creator visit this sin-cursed world in the person of Jesus Christ of Nazareth in order to redeem men from sin and its curse. For the Bible says: "God so loved the world that He gave His only begotten son, that whosoever believeth in Him should not perish but have everlasting life." And Jesus Christ said: "I am come that they might have life, and that they might have it more abundantly." And in another place "If any man thirst let him come unto me and drink", and again, "As many as received Him, to them gave He power to become the sons of God".

This is no idle philosophy or visionary dream or religious jargon. The Creator's coming into the world, His birth, life, death and resurrection were prophesied hundreds of years before He ever came. These prophecies were fulfilled and have now become historical facts. And the effect of His coming has been to change the course of history. This is not all. The fact of Christ is also experimental; and in this sense it is scientific! Everyone who is prepared to believe and commit his life to Christ can experience His power in his life. "The man who has received my commands and obeys them – he it is who loves me: and he who loves me will be loved of my father: and *I will love him and disclose myself to* him" (New English Bible, John 14: 21). And such manifestation of the Creator to the human heart delivers man from his bondage of sin and opens his eyes to the realities of the spiritual world. Only then he comes to know the Creator and the truth of His creation, as recorded in the Bible.

Then he shall know that "by Him (Jesus Christ) were all things created, that are in heaven, and that are in the earth, visible and invisible . . . all things were created by Him and for Him. And He is before all things and by Him all things consist". And then he will not be deceived by "profane and vain babblings and oppositions of science falsely so called".

The reason why so many oppose the doctrine of creation is often due to prejudice or careless reading. Careful reading of the Scriptures, with an open mind, will reveal that no established scientific fact contradicts the story of creation as described in the first chapter of the Bible. On the other hand, such a study will show that the doctrine of creation, the doctrine of sin, and the catastrophe of the Noachic flood as stated in the Bible, alone can reconcile all the facts of cosmology, cosmogony, the origin of life, its reproducing only "after its kind", its variation within limits, and all the facts of Palaeontology. The facts of Palaeontology, namely, the sudden and violent entombment of animals leaving millions of fossils aggregated together and others preserved in ice in the very act of feeding, can, in fact, be explained only in terms of a universal flood as described in the Bible. Geological strata with their fossils indicate not the order of evolution or even creation, but the order of burial in the waters of that deluge.

These facts of science can harmoniously be blended only in terms of creation. The doctrine of creation not only harmonises demonstrable facts of science, but also the truths of the spiritual realm, which is ignored by the protagonists of evolution. Truly "all things were made by Him and without Him was not anything made that was made". For it is the same Creator who inspired the prophet to write the account of creation.

BIBLIOGRAPHY

1. *Methods of Study in Natural History* by Louis Agassiz.
2. *Genetics and the Origin of Species* by T. Dobshansky.
3. *A Critique on Evolution Theory* by T. H. Morgan.
4. *Limitations of Science* by J. W. N. Sullivan.
5. *The Principles of Heredity* by L. H. Snyden.
6. *Evolution and Living Organisms* by Professor E. S. Goodrich.
7. *Principles of Stratigraphy* by Grabau.
8. *Geological Biology* by H. S. Williams.
9. *Nuclear Geology* by Henry Faul.
10. *Physics of the Earth* by Professor Arthur Holmes.
11. *Evolution, Genetics and Eugenics* by H. H. Newman.
12. *Extinct Plants and Problems of Evolution* by Dr. D. H. Scott.
13. *Cambridge Natural History*, Vol. III by Professor A. H. Cook.
14. *Transformations of the Animal World* by Charles Duperette.
15. *Biology and its Makers* by Professor Locy.
16. *What the Animal Fossils Tell Us* by Douglas Dewar.
17. *Outlines of Comparative Anatomy* by Professor A. Richards.
18. *Human Body* by Sir Arthur Keith.
19. *Darwinism Today* by W. L. Kellog.
20. *Science Remaking the World* by J. M. Coulter.
21. *Material Basis of Evolution* by Goldschmidt.
22. *Scientific Basis of Evolution* by T. H. Morgan.
23. *The Problem of the Origin of Species since Darwin* (*Hereditas*, vol. 120, 1936) by H. Nilsson.
24. *Synthetic Speciation* (in German, 1954) by H. Nilsson.
25. *The Genesis of Drosophila* by T. H. Morgan.
26. *Tempo and Mode of Evolution* (1944) by George Gaylord Simpson.

124

27. *An Introduction to Palaeontology* by Chester A. Arnold.

28. *The Major Feature of Evolution* (1953), by G. G. Simpson.

29. *Genetics, Palaeontology and Evolution* (1949), by D. Dwight Davies.

30. *Evolution and Adaptation* by T. H. Morgan.

31. *The Next War* by General Von Bernhardi.

32. *Evolution implies Atheism* by Vice-Chairman, A.A.A.A., Mr. Woolsey Teller.

33. *This is Serious*, Pamphlet by Newman Watts.

34. *The Bible* (Authorised Version) and *The New English Bible.*

35. *A New Critique of the Transformist Principle* (1964), by Dr. J. J. Duyveen De Wit.

36. *Evolution or Creation?* by Sir Ambrose Fleming, KT, M.A., D.SC., F.R.S.

37. *Difficulties of the Theory of Evolution* by Douglas Dewar.

38. *More Difficulties of the Theory of Evolution* by Douglas Dewar.

39. *A Challenge to Evolutionists* by Douglas Dewar.

40. *Is Evolution Proved?* by Dewar and Shelton.

41. All pamphlets issued by *Evolution Protest Movement.*

42. *After Its Kind* (The first and the last word of Evolution) by Byron C. Nelson, TH.M.

43. *Predicament of Evolution* by George McReady Price.

44. *A History of Some Scientific Blunders* by George McReady Price.

45. *Fundamentals of Geology* by George McReady Price.

46. *Back to the Bible or The New Protestantism* by George McReady Price.

47. *Genesis Vindicated* by George McReady Price.

48. *The Biblical Story of Creation* by Giorgio Bartoli.

49. *Does Science support Evolution?* by E. Ralph Hooper.

50. *Evolution and the Break up of Christendom* by C. Leopold Clarke.

51. *Evolution, Creation and Science* by Dr. Frank L. Marsh.

52. *Life, Man and Time* by Dr. Frank L. Marsh.

53. *Modern Science and the Genesis Record* by Harry Rimmer.

54. *The Harmony of Science and Scripture* by Harry Rimmer.

55. *Lot's Wife* by Harry Rimmer.

56. *Modern Science and Christian Faith* by Members of the American Scientific Association.

57. *The Christian View of Science and Scripture* by Members of the American Scientific Association.

58. *The Bible and Modern Science* by Dr. L. Merson Davies.

59. *Why be an Ape?* by "A London Journalist".
60. *The Story of Creation*, edited by Russell Mixter.
61. *Why I believe in Creation not in Evolution* by Fred John Meldan. Editor *Christian Victory* Magazine.
62. *Is Evolution a Myth?* by Douglas Dewar, Merson Davies and Professor J. B. S. Haldane.
63. *Creation Revealed in Six Days* by P. J. Wiseman.
64. *New Discoveries in Babylonia about Genesis* by P. J. Wiseman.
65. *Creation and Evolution* by Dr. John Lever.
66. *The Genesis Flood* by Henry M. Morris and John C. Whitcomb, Jr.
67. *The Origin of Species* (1963 edition) with introduction by Professor W. R. Thompson, F.R.S.
68. *Biblical Catastrophism and Geology* by Henry M. Morris, PH.D.
69. *Papers, Journals, Magazines, etc.*
    (a) Pamphlets of the *Evolution Protest Movement*.
    (b) *Nature*.
    (c) *Quarterly Review of Biology*.
    (d) *Journal of Genetics*.
    (e) *Time*.
    (f) *American Nature*.
    (g) *Science* by Professor J. Holmes.
    (h) *Complete Works of Neitzsche*.
    (i) *Annual Report of A.A.A.A.* by Charles Smith.
    (j) *Creation Research Society Annual* (1964) and other publications.
70. *Radio-carbon Dating* (1952), by W. F. Libby (University of Chicago Press, Chicago, U.S.A.).
71. *Radio-carbon Dating* (1955), by W. F. Libby (Second Edition).
72. *P. Seven* (1955), by W. F. Libby.
73. *Radio-carbon confirms Biblical Creation* (Creation Research Society Quarterly, Vol. 5, No. 2, September 1968) by Robert L. Whitelaw.
74. *Time, Life and History in the Light of 15,000 Radio-carbon Dates* (Creation Research Society, Quarterly Vol. 7, No. 1, June 1970) by Robert L. Whitelaw.
75. *Remains of Hominidae from Pliocene Pleistocene Formation in The Lower Omobasin*, Ethiopia Nature 223:1234 (1969) by F. C. Howell.
76. *On the Relationship between Radio-carbon Dates and True Sample*

Ages. Radio-carbon 8:534 (1966) by Stuiver, Ninze and Hans Suess.

77. *Time, Life and History in the Light of 15,000 Radio-carbon Dates* (1970). Creation Research Society Quarterly, Vol. 7, No. 1, page 56 (1968); Radio-carbon Confirms Biblical Creation C.R.S. Vol. 5, No. 2 (1968) by R. L. Whitelaw.

78. *The Fundamentals of Geology* by George McReady Price.

79. *The Genesis Flood* (1961) by John C. Whitcomb and Henry M. Morris.

80. *Potassium Argon Dating* (1966) by O. A. Shaeffer and J. Zahringer. (Springer Verlag, New York.)